GRADE 7

g.u.m. drops
(GRAMMAR, USAGE, & MECHANICS)

90 Reproducible Worksheets Based around Editing
Passages from Classic Literature

by

Melissa L. Schneider

www.inthethinkofthings.com   ISBN 1-933407-05-0

5415 Regency Way   Printed in the United States

Rockford, IL 61114   of America

Copyright 2007

To the Teacher:

The G.U.M. Drops workbooks were designed to be used as daily supplements. Each workbook is exactly 90 pages long and is roughly divided into 18 weeks. This makes the workbooks ideal to use every day for one semester. However, because the pages continually build upon each other, you can easily adapt the books to fit your schedule by doing more than one page at a time or doing a page every other day. The workbooks are written directly to the student so that they can complete the exercises unassisted. If they do require additional help, there are notes on many of the teacher pages so that you can help them work through the concepts. The number of errors is also included on the teacher pages, which you may or may not choose to share with the student in order to make the exercises easier/harder.

Contents

Complete Sentences

A complete sentence has a subject and a predicate.

The **subject** is the part of the sentence that tells *who* or *what* the sentence is about. The simple subject is the main noun or pronoun. The **predicate** is the part of the sentence that tells *what the subject did* or *gives more information* about the subject. The simple predicate is the verb/verb phrase. If a sentence does not have both a subject and a predicate, it is not a complete sentence. It is a **sentence fragment**.

simple simple

<u>The train blew its whistle early in the morning.</u>   <u>Was not awake yet.</u>

subject   predicate   fragment - no subject

Run-on sentences occur when phrases are joined (or run together) without any punctuation or connecting words or with too many connecting words.

> We bought popcorn and cheered a lot at the circus and then we left.

> I liked the circus I want to go back next year.

Identify run-ons or fragments. In the others, underline the complete subject once and complete predicate twice. Circle each simple subject and simple predicate.

Three large barn cats. F

I saw a picture of a giant snake.

The four sisters played a card game.

Joel lives in California he likes swimming in the ocean and sand volleyball. RO

The thin brown curtains fluttered in the cool breeze.

Scurried up an old oak tree. F

The crickets chirped all day and all night.

1

Read this passage from *Around the World in Eighty Days*. Identify any run-on sentences. Make sure each underlined sentence is complete. If it is, circle the simple subject and the simple predicate. If it is not, identify the fragment as a subject (s) or a predicate (p).

Phileas Fogg lived in London in 1872. Resided in a house on Saville Row with just one servant. Phileas Fogg was a member of the esteemed Reform Club. Beyond that, very little was known about him. He was rich, for sure, but no one knew how he had become wealthy. He seemed to be very knowledgeable about other countries and cultures, but no one could remember him leaving London in many years.

One day Phileas Fogg. He had a very exact, punctual nature. His daily routine was followed to the minute, without any variance in his activities. He spent a good part of each day at the Reform Club where he read newspapers and ate fine meals and played whist a card game of which he was very fond.

Because Phileas Fogg spent so much time at the Reform Club, his servant had very little to do. However, Phileas expected his man to be extraordinarily exact. On October 2, 1872, Phileas dismissed his present servant. Had brought Phileas shaving water two degrees too cold.

Sentence Types

There are four types of sentences.

All sentences begin with a capital letter. However, the punctuation at the end of the sentence depends on what type of sentence it is.

Declarative sentences are statements. They end with periods.

    There are many different kinds of sharks.

Imperative sentences are commands. They also end with periods. The subject, you, is suggested but not directly stated.

    Stay away from sharks.

Interrogative sentences are questions. They end with question marks.

    Have you ever seen a shark?

Exclamatory sentences are full of emotion. They end with exclamation points.

    Here comes a shark!

Add capital letters and ending punctuation to the sentences below. Identify the type of each one.

go to bed   _Go to bed._

my purse was stolen   _My purse was stolen._

how do you like your eggs   _How do you like your eggs?_

shut the cabinet   _Shut the cabinet._

our house has a big basement   _Are you scared of the dark?_

are you scared of the dark   _____

the barn is on fire   _The barn is on fire!_

Edit this passage from *Around the World in Eighty Days* by adding capital letters and ending punctuation where needed. Use all three types of ending punctuation.

that same morning a Frenchman by the name of Passepartout came to apply for a job. Passepartout was looking for a quiet life as a servant He knew that Phileas Fogg was a man with an exact routine, and he was pleased when Phileas hired him.

at exactly half past eleven, Phileas Fogg left for the Reform Club as he did every day. passepartout found a card outlining the details of his master's routine and the daily duties expected of the servant.

That night Phileas Fogg played whist with his usual partners Their conversation revolved around a recent bank robbery. The thief had stolen fifty-five thousand pounds Phileas's friends began to argue about the chances of the man being caught. Fogg remarked that it was now possible to go around the world in only eighty days. this started a new argument, which ended with Phileas betting twenty thousand pounds on his remark. His friends accepted. Phileas Fogg stated that he would return to the club in exactly eighty days, on Saturday, December 21, 1872.

Passepartout was shocked what had happened to his quiet life

Review Time!

Edit this passage from *Around the World in Eighty Days*. Underline any sentence fragments and identify them as subjects (s) or predicates (p).

the remarkable wager of Phileas Fogg quickly spread throughout the Reform Club and all of England. People chose sides and made wagers of their own with their friends Most people bet against Fogg, especially after a certain telegram was received in London. it said that Detective Fix of the Scotland Yard had found the bank robber and was following him. The robber's name was Phileas Fogg

Put a stop to the betting. People began to talk about the strange habits of Phileas Fogg. His mysterious ways seemed suspicious. they thought he'd made the wager simply to escape.

Detective Fix had seen Phileas Fogg and Passepartout in Egypt He had been on the wharf when they arrived by ship. Phileas fit the description of the bank robber, and Detective Fix was convinced from the first moment that he was indeed the thief. he sent a telegram to the police in London asking them to send a warrant to Bombay. He planned to follow Phileas to Bombay, get the warrant, and arrest him at once

Nouns

Nouns are words that name a person, place, thing, or idea.

Common nouns name general people, places, things, or ideas.

woman   mountains   truck   soccer

Proper nouns name specific people, places, things, or ideas. They are capitalized.

Mrs. Ly   Rocky Mountains   Dodge Ram   World Cup

Concrete nouns are physical. They can be seen, heard, touched, smelled, or tasted. Concrete nouns may be common or proper.

bacon   Statue of Liberty   bird   Bible

Abstract nouns are things that cannot be seen, heard, touched, smelled, or tasted. They name ideas, conditions, or feelings.

liberty   hope   childhood   courage

Identify the nouns in the first column as common or proper. Identify the nouns in the second column as concrete or abstract.

restaurant C   relaxation A

Speckles P   whisper C

Hawaii P   wisdom A

grandparents C   money C

rose C   rose C

year C   scent C

World War I P   opportunity A

Read this passage from *Around the World in Eighty Days*. Circle at least fifteen common nouns. Underline and capitalize the proper nouns.

fix befriended passepartout in order to find out more about the mysterious phileas fogg. passepartout was completely unaware of the detective's schemes and was only too happy to find a friend.

The ship to bombay, india arrived two days early. phileas fogg recorded the fact in his notebook and calmly went to the passport office to get his passport marked. detective fix went to the police, where he learned that the warrant had not yet arrived.

phileas, passepartout, and sir frances cromarty, a fellow passenger from the ship, took the train from bombay to calcutta. However, the rails had not quite been completed, and the passengers were forced to find another source of transportation. passepartout thought that this delay would ruin them, but phileas was not put out in the least. He found a man with a trained elephant and bought it for two thousand pounds - an extraordinary amount! passepartout was speechless. phileas hired an elephant driver and kindly invited sir frances cromarty to join them.

Capitalization

Here are more words that are always capitalized:

days of the week	Tuesday
months of the year	October
holidays	Mother's Day
titles of people	Uncle Roger
people's initials (also marked with periods)	Joyce L. Kent
the pronoun "I"	Yes, I will go with you.
titles of works	The Wizard of Oz

Proper adjectives are also capitalized. Proper adjectives are descriptive words formed from proper nouns.

Spanish lace   Kansas prairie   German chocolate

Abbreviated proper nouns remain capitalized. They are marked with periods.

Friday > Fri.   Professor > Prof.   Misses > Mrs.

Add capital letters and periods where they belong in the sentences below.

on saturday my dad and i are going to an illinois football game

she got a dell computer for christmas

next january our family is going on a caribbean cruise

our neighbor, lieut j harrison, owns four german shepherds

aunt janice is coming to visit on the third wednesday in march

she introduced herself as mrs patricia m jackson

before i went to bed, i read two chapters in my book

Edit this passage from *Around the World in Eighty Days*.

The elephant driver knew the calcutta countryside well and was determined to make the trip as quickly as possible. However, late on saturday afternoon they heard something. It was a brahmin funeral procession. They hid amongst the trees and watched the brahmins pass. Some of them were leading a beautiful young woman, who kept trying to break away. When the brahmins had disappeared from sight, their guide told them what was happening. The young woman had been forced to marry a rajah. He had died, and now the brahmins were going to sacrifice her at his funeral!

mr phileas fogg simply suggested, "Let's save her."

passepartout and sir frances agreed. They waited until night, but the guards did not go to sleep. In the early morning the funeral started. phileas fogg was just about to run into the crowd when the people all fell facedown. The dead rajah had risen up, taken his wife in his arms, and was walking away

When the rajah came closer, phileas recognized passepartout. He had daringly snuck in to the camp to rescue the unconscious young woman! They quickly boarded the elephant and set off, narrowly avoiding capture.

Review Time!

Edit this passage from *Around the World in Eighty Days*.

The young woman's name was aouda, and she was quite charming. She was the daughter of a rich merchant and had received an english education. She spoke English very well and was extremely grateful to her rescuers. She agreed to accompany them to hong kong, where she had a relative who would take care of her.

When they reached their destination, phileas gave the elephant to the driver, who had proved most faithful.

det fix was waiting for Phileas in calcutta. He was again unable to detain him, so he continued to follow him. He boarded the same ship, which would take the passengers from india to hong kong

Passepartout saw the detective on the ship, and he became suspicious. He decided that fix had been sent by the members of the reform club to make sure Phileas Fogg actually went around the world.

Due to the stormy october weather, the steamship arrived a day late. Therefore, phileas fogg missed the ship to japan.

Plural Nouns

Plural nouns name more than one person, place, thing, or idea.

You can make most nouns plural just by adding **"s."**

napkin > napkin<u>s</u>   chief > chief<u>s</u>   day > day<u>s</u>

If a noun ends with **"ch," "sh," "s," "x," or "z,"** add **"es"** to make it plural.

switch > switch<u>es</u>   boss > boss<u>es</u>   buzz > buzz<u>es</u>

If a noun ends with **a consonant and then "y,"** change the **"y"** to **"i"** and add **"es."**

battery > batter<u>ies</u>   belly > bell<u>ies</u>   trophy > troph<u>ies</u>

If a noun ends with **"f" or "fe" and makes a "v" sound in the plural**, change the **"f"** to **"v"** and end it with **"es."**   wife > wi<u>ves</u>   half > hal<u>ves</u>

Irregular plural nouns don't follow any rules at all.

woman > women   sheep > sheep   person > people

Collective nouns name a collection of people, places, things, or ideas.

group   pile   United States   community

Read the nouns below. Write the plural forms in the blanks provided.

crutch _____   child _____   calf _____

deer _____   library _____   engine _____

dish _____   mouse _____   camera _____

chef _____   man _____   mess _____

Edit this passage from *Around the World in Eighty Days*. Cross out any misspelled plural nouns and write the correct plural nouns above.

As it turned out, Aouda's relative had left Hong Kong and was now living with some other familys in holland. Phileas Fogg invited aouda to travel back to europe with them, and she was delighted. She had grown quite attached to mr phileas fogg, and her eyes lit up with respect and love for him. Phileas seemed unaware of her affection, but he made sure she was as comfortable as possible and that her few wishs were met.

The travelers went through a series of adventures after landing in Hong Kong The long and short of it was that despite getting separated for a while, Phileas, Aouda, Passepartout, and detective fix all managed to board a steamship bound for california.

Detective Fix had to wait until Phileas Fogg was back on english soil in order to arrest him. He told passepartout who he really was. Passepartout was outraged However, Detective Fix explained that he now wanted Phileas to make it back to london as quickly as possible, and the two became allys.

Verbs

Verbs are words that show action or complete a thought.

Action verbs tell the action of the subject.

She <u>touched</u> the snail.   The dog <u>wagged</u> his tail.

My brother <u>laughed</u>.   Cody <u>took</u> a piece of candy.

Linking verbs link the subject to a noun, pronoun, or adjective that describes the subject. They complete a thought. They do not show action.

They <u>are</u> our neighbors.   I <u>felt</u> thirsty.

That snake <u>is</u> colorful.   She <u>became</u> angry.

Helping verbs come before the main verb and help describe the action or show the time of the action.

Melody <u>is</u> building a birdhouse.   They <u>were</u> singing a carol.

I <u>can</u> feed the fish.   Mom <u>will</u> make supper.

Circle all of the verbs in the sentences below. Identify them as action (a), linking (l), or helping (h) verbs.

My cousin may arrive two days early.

Dad looked funny in the top hat.

We were very content.

She was arranging the flowers in a vase.

The whale splashed everyone in the front row.

Dr. Wise will be performing the surgery.

Read this passage from *Around the World in Eighty Days*. Identify the underlined verbs as action (a), helping (h), or linking (l) verbs.

Phileas Fogg and company <u>were</u> <u>traveling</u> by train to New York. In Nebraska, Indians <u>attacked</u> the train. The conductor was left unconscious, and the train <u>was</u> <u>traveling</u> at a very high speed. If it couldn't be stopped at the Fort Kearney station, all would be lost!

When Passepartout heard this, he <u>slipped</u> underneath the train. He carefully crawled from car to car until he reached the engine. He managed to unhook it, and it continued on alone while the rest of the train <u>slowed</u> to a stop just short of the Fort Kearney station. When the passengers were counted, three of them <u>were</u> missing, including Passepartout. Despite the fact that the next train wouldn't wait, Phileas <u>led</u> a band of thirty men to find the missing passengers. He <u>was</u> determined to find them.

After a successful rescue mission, Phileas <u>returned</u> to the Fort Kearney station. Phileas, Passepartout, Aouda, and Fix boarded a unique vehicle called a sledge, which <u>would</u> <u>whisk</u> them away to Omaha in enough time to catch the next train. Thankfully, the rest of the journey to New York passed without excitement.

Review Time!

Edit this passage from *Around the World in Eighty Days*.

When Phileas Fogg reached new york, he learned that he had missed the steamship to England by just forty-five minutes While the rest of the group began to complain, Phileas set off right away to find out which countrys other ships were going to. He found a ship bound for france. He and the others boarded the steamer.

The next day the captain was outraged to find the ship on a course to England! Phileas Fogg had paid the crew to take him to england. The captain was powerless and angry, but Phileas calmed him by buying the ship for much more than it was worth.

Phileas arrived in England on the 21st before noon The group sat down to their lunchs. Phileas had more than enough time to make it to london. Just then Detective Fix put a hand on Phileas's shoulder.

"You're under arrest," Detective Fix said, and he took Phileas to prison.

Nearly two hours later det fix rushed in to see Phileas Fogg.

"I'm sorry!" he yelled, "You're free The robber was found three days ago!"

Verb Tenses

Verbs tell what happened in the past, what is happening
at present, or what will happen in the future.

Past tense verbs tell about events that happened in the past.

Simple Past - no helping verbs, often ends in "ed" >   He <u>entered</u> the room.

Past Perfect - uses verb "had"   >   He <u>had entered</u> the room.

Past Progressive - uses verb "was" or "were"   >   He <u>was entering</u> the room.

Present tense verbs tell about events that are happening right now, in the present.

Simple Present - no helping verbs   >   He <u>enters</u> the room.

Present Perfect - uses verb "has" or "have"   >   He <u>has entered</u> the room.

Present Progressive - uses verb "is" "am" or "are"   >   He <u>is entering</u> the room.

Future tense verbs tell about events that will happen in the future.

Simple Future - uses verb "will" or "shall"   >   He <u>shall enter</u> the room.

Future Perfect - uses verbs "will/shall have"   >   He <u>will have entered</u> the room.

Future Progressive - uses verbs "will/shall be"   >   He <u>will be entering</u> the room.

Identify the complete tense of each verb/verb phrase underlined below.

She <u>shall have raked</u> the yard.   _____

The twins <u>raced</u> to the playhouse.   _____

I <u>will be sewing</u> a dress for the play. _____

They <u>had walked</u> home from the park.   _____

Seth <u>is cleaning</u> up the mess.   _____

Read this passage from *Around the World in Eighty Days*. Identify the complete tense of each underlined verb/verb phrase.

Phileas Fogg and his friends <u>boarded</u> a train and sped towards London. When they stepped off the train, the clocks <u>were striking</u> ten minutes before nine. Phileas was just five minutes late!

The next evening Phileas told Aouda he was sorry he <u>had brought</u> her to England, as he was now poor. Aouda asked Phileas to marry her. She had grown to love him and did not care that he was poor now. Phileas loved Aouda in return, so he sent Passepartout to the reverend's house.

Passepartout came rushing back. He grabbed Phileas and said, "Sir, it <u>is</u> not Sunday! It's Saturday! You must go to the Reform Club! You <u>will have won</u> the bet!"

Phileas had made a mistake! By traveling continually eastward, he had gained an entire day. He thought he <u>had arrived</u> in London on Saturday night at ten to nine, but it had been Friday night at ten to nine!

He rushed to the Reform Club, and at precisely 8:45 on Saturday, December 21, he <u>was standing</u> before his astonished whist partners. He won the bet and <u>received</u> twenty thousand pounds.

Phileas Fogg had made it around the world in eighty days!

Irregular Verbs

Irregular verbs do not have an -ed ending in the past tense.

Irregular verbs don't follow any rules at all; they simply have to be learned.

   break > broke   do > did   give > gave   write > wrote

Another verb form is the **past participle**. This verb form means past or completed action. In <u>regular</u> verbs the past participle is the same as the simple past tense, but it is used with one of the following helping verbs: has, have, or had.

   She <u>mopped</u> the floor.   >   She <u>had mopped</u> the floor.

In <u>irregular</u> verbs the past participle often changes completely from simple past tense.

   The bird <u>flew</u> away.   >   The bird <u>had</u> <u>flown</u> away.

   She <u>woke</u> up early.   >   She <u>has</u> <u>woken</u> up early.

   He <u>rode</u> the horse.   >   He <u>will</u> <u>have</u> <u>ridden</u> the horse.

The past participle with "had" forms past perfect tense.   I <u>had</u> <u>gone</u>.

The past participle with "has" or "have" forms present perfect tense.   She <u>has</u> <u>gone</u>.

The past participle with "will have" forms future perfect tense.   He <u>will</u> <u>have</u> <u>gone</u>.

Write the past tense and past participle of each present tense verb.

(blow) Yesterday I _____ a bubble. I had _____ a bubble.

(fall)   Yesterday I _____ down. I had _____ down.

(give) Yesterday I _____ a dime. I had _____ a dime.

(see)   Yesterday I _____ a deer. I had _____ a deer.

(take) Yesterday I _____ a bath. I had _____ a bath.

Read this passage from *The Last of the Mohicans*. Cross out any incorrect irregular verbs and write the correct verbs above.

The French and English were fighting for control of North America. The colonists fighted with the English; many of the Indian tribes fought with the French. Colonel Munro was the commander of Fort William Henry, one of the English forts. He sended a letter to General Webb, the commander of Fort Edward, asking him to bring reinforcements immediately. The French army, under the command of Montcalm, was advancing toward Fort William Henry. Munro knowed he would need more men for the upcoming battle.

Munro's beautiful daughters, Cora and Alice, were also at Fort Edward. They were leaving for Fort William Henry to join their father. Major Duncan Heyward rode along with them as their guardian. Another man, David Gamut, was also traveling with them. He singed Psalms. The little party was being leaded by an Indian runner, Magua. He was a friend to the English and taked the group to Fort William Henry by way of a shortcut through the woods.

Review Time!

Edit this passage from *The Last of the Mohicans*.

Just two miles west, two men sitted and talked. One of them was a white man, although his face was sunburned and worn as though he spent a lot of time outdoors. He was dressed ruggedly and carried a rifle and a knife. His name was hawkeye, and he was a scout. He had lived with the Indians for most of his life. The man he was talking with was an indian named Chingachgook. Hawkeye and chingachgook were great friends, closer than brothers.

Chingachgook had a son named uncas. They were the last of their people, the Mohicans. The three mans had been living and hunting together for a long time. Uncas joined his father and Hawkeye, and they beginned to eat supper.

meanwhile, the small party of travelers comed close to where the three men were eating. Duncan asked the scout if they were near fort william henry. Hawkeye replied that they were going in the wrong direction. When Hawkeye saw Magua, he recognized him as a Huron. Hawkeye told Duncan that the hurons were a thievish people and could not be trusted. The men tried to catch magua, but he escaped into the woods.

Subject / Verb Agreement

The subject and verb in a sentence have to agree.

In present tense the verb changes to agree with the subject. If the subject is plural, the verb must be plural. If the subject is singular, the verb must be singular. Most singular verbs end with "s." The singular subjects "I" and "you" do <u>not</u> follow this rule.

> The girls <u>kick</u> the ball.   The girl <u>kicks</u> the ball.
>
> I <u>kick</u> the ball.   You <u>kick</u> the ball.

Compound subjects (two or more) use a plural verb when connected by "and."

> Dad and the girls <u>kick</u> the ball.   The girls and Dad <u>kick</u> the ball.

If a compound subject is joined by "or" or "nor," the verb must agree with the subject that is closest to the verb whether it is singular or plural.

Either Dad or the girls <u>kick</u> the ball.   Either the girls or Dad <u>kicks</u> the ball.

Some forms of the verb "to be" change form in past and present tense.

> He <u>was</u> fast.   I <u>was</u> fast.   You <u>were</u> fast.   They <u>were</u> fast.

Circle the correct verbs in the sentences below.

They (walk / walks) everyday. He (walk / walks) faster than she does.

My brother (is / am) tired. I (is / am) tired too.

Neither Mom nor my aunts (cook / cooks) supper on Fridays.

Do you (throw / throws) very far? She (throw / throws) really far.

Libby (clean / cleans) her room often. I never (clean / cleans) mine.

I (is / am / are) leaving. (Is / Am / Are) you going with me?

Edit this passage from *The Last of the Mohicans*. Circle the correct verbs.

   When Duncan Heyward realized that they had been deceived and betrayed by magua, he didn't know what to do. He (was / were) responsible for the safety of the two sisters. He asked Hawkeye and his companions for help After a short discussion, Hawkeye announced that they were willing to lead the party to fort william henry.

   Hawkeye, Chingachgook, and uncas (was / were) capable, trustworthy, and caring. Knowing that Magua would return with more Hurons, they led their new friends to a secret hiding place. It was a cave with hidden entrances surrounded by waterfalls.

   For a while the group was able to rest However, soon the hurons returned. The men fought well, but eventually Hawkeye, Chingachgook, and Uncas knowed that they would be overcome. There was nothing to do now but hide in the cave. Although the brave men were prepared to fight to the death, Cora urged them to try and escape.

   "If you (escape / escapes)," she said, "you can send help for us. If Magua (capture / captures) all of us, there will be no hope of being rescued!"

Verbals

Verbals are similar to verbs, but they function as other parts of speech.

Verbals are formed from verbs and have the power of verbs, but they instead function as nouns, adjectives, and adverbs. There are three types of verbals.

A **gerund** is a verb form ending in "ing" and is used as a noun.

> <u>Fishing</u> is very relaxing.   My dad enjoys <u>fishing</u> on Saturdays.

An **infinitive** is a verb form usually consisting of a verb preceded by the word "to" and may be used as a noun, an adjective, or an adverb.

> <u>To sing</u> in front of an audience would be scary.

> I do not have the courage <u>to sing</u> on stage.

A **participle** is a verb form often ending in "ing" or "ed" and is used as an adjective.

> The crowd of <u>screaming</u> people moved slowly up the street.

> The stacks of <u>counted</u> bills were locked in the safe.

Identify the types of verbals underlined in the sentences below.

I gave the <u>sleeping</u> baby to his mother.   _____

<u>Bowling</u> is one of my favorite sports.   _____

My mom wants <u>to read</u> all of the classics.   _____

<u>To live</u> in medieval times would have been exciting. _____

The group of <u>smiling</u> customers left a nice tip.   _____

I started <u>skiing</u> two years ago.   _____

Read this passage from *The Last of the Mohicans*. Identify the underlined verbals as gerunds (g), infinitives (i), or participles (p).

Although they didn't want to leave, Hawkeye and the Mohicans realized that Cora was right. Escaping was their only chance. They dropped into the swirling water and disappeared from sight. Cora tried to convince Duncan to follow them, but he refused to leave the girls. Instead, Duncan and Cora did their best to calm crying Alice. She was very frightened and shook uncontrollably.

The four travelers hid as deep in the cave as they could, but eventually Magua and the Hurons found them. They dragged them out of the cave. Cora and Alice were put on rested horses, while Duncan and David were made to walk. They did not know what the Hurons planned to do with them.

When they stopped for a meal, Cora bravely approached Magua. She asked him to release Alice and pour out his anger on herself. Asking was not easy! Magua replied that he would let Alice go if Cora would consent to be his wife and live in his wigwam. Cora was disgusted by the offer. She told Duncan and Alice what he had said. In a moment of strength, Alice replied that it would be better for them to die together.

Review Time!

Edit this passage from *The Last of the Mohicans*. Identify the underlined verbals as gerunds (g), infinitives (i), or participles (p).

When cora refused Magua's offer, he announced that they would all be killed. One of the Indians approached Alice. Duncan angrily jumped on him, but the Indian (was / were) too strong. just before the Huron could sink his knife into Duncan, the sound of a rifle echoed through the woods. The Indian fell down dead. Hawkeye, Chingachgook, and Uncas charged into the camp! <u>Fighting</u> broke out immediately. Only Magua managed <u>to escape</u>, wounded but alive. The three warriors explained that after escaping down the river, they had hidden nearby. Uncas had finded the <u>fleeing</u> Hurons' trail, and they had followed them, waiting for a chance to rescue the group.

Although there were both Huron and french enemys between them and fort william henry, Hawkeye and his companions (was / were) able <u>to escort</u> the group safely to the fort. colonel munro was delighted to be reunited with his daughters. Duncan Heyward was also glad to be back. He wanted to ask the colonel for permission to marry Alice

Pronouns

Pronouns replace nouns.

An **objective pronoun** replaces a noun that is an object in a sentence.

A **nominative pronoun** replaces a noun that is the subject of a sentence.

Marianne likes to play sports. She is good at them.

A **reflexive pronoun** refers back to a noun or pronoun in the sentence. Reflexive pronouns include myself, yourself, himself, herself, itself, themselves, and ourselves.

The children entertained themselves while the adults talked.

A **demonstrative pronoun** points out a noun without naming the noun. Demonstrative pronouns include this, that, these, and those.

That was very sad. I got this for my birthday.

An **indefinite pronoun** does not name the noun it replaces. Indefinite pronouns include everyone, anything, somebody, none, either, all, some, both, many, and most.

Everyone went home early. Something is wrong.

An **interrogative pronoun** asks a question without naming the noun. Interrogative pronouns include who, whose, whom, which, and what.

Who knocked on the door? Which do you want?

Circle all of the pronouns in the sentences below.

Simon drove himself home. Someone went with him. Who was it?

Those are very noisy. They are singing. Both are too loud.

Abigail went to bed. She was tired. I am tired myself.

We are late. No one was ready. Whom should we apologize to?

Edit this passage from *The Last of the Mohicans*. Circle the correct pronouns.

Although Munro was overjoyed by the presence of his daughters, all was not well. (They / Them) were under attack from the French, and so far no help had arrived from fort edward.

Colonel Munro met with the leader of the french army, Montcalm. The French had captured a messenger on his way to Fort William Henry. Montcalm showed a letter to colonel munro. It (was / were) from general webb, and it said that (he / him) was not sending reinforcements. He advised Colonel Munro to surrender to Montcalm.

Munro was prepared to fight bravely to the end, but Montcalm offered him a peaceful compromise. The English had to leave the fort, but montcalm would allow (they / them) to take their arms and colors with them. In this way the english army would maintain their dignity, and both armys would be spared unnecessary bloodshed.

Pronoun / Antecedent Agreement

Pronouns must agree with the nouns they replace.

An **antecedent** is a word being replaced or referred to by a pronoun. The pronoun must agree in number and gender with the antecedent.

If the antecedent is singular, the pronoun must be singular.

The <u>boy</u> built a snowman. <u>He</u> built a very fat snowman.

The boy built a snow <u>fort</u>. <u>It</u> was very sturdy.

If the antecedent is plural, the pronoun must be plural.

The <u>boys</u> built a snowman. <u>They</u> built it all by <u>themselves</u>.

The boys built two snow <u>forts</u>. The boys built <u>them</u> quickly.

If the antecedent is **masculine** (referring to a boy or man), the pronoun must be masculine. If the antecedent is **feminine** (referring to a girl or woman), the pronoun must be feminine.

My <u>mom</u> has three sisters. <u>She</u> doesn't have any brothers.

<u>Vince</u> bought his aunt a present. <u>He</u> picked it out <u>himself</u>.

Circle the correct pronouns in the sentences below.

My uncle and cousin are coming. (He / They) are coming today.

I am building a shelf. (I / Me) am building it all by (itself / myself).

The class starts in the fall. (It / They) lasts for three months.

He took the dogs for a walk. (It / They) love going for walks.

Isaac grilled some hotdogs. (He / She) ate (it / them) all.

Edit this passage from *The Last of the Mohicans*. Circle the correct pronouns.

While the french were satisfied with the agreement, their indian allies were not. They had expected to be rewarded with loot from those they killed in the fighting. This new arrangement didn't offer (him / them) the opportunity to gain anything.

The Indians waited as the english army moved away from the fort. They watched with greedy eyes. Cora noticed magua moving amongst (they / them). Suddenly the Indians began ripping clothing and other trinkets away from the English. Magua let out a piercing war cry, and the attack began in earnest. Dozens of womans, childs, and soldiers (was / were) killed. Magua recognized Cora and Alice. He put them on horses and led them into the forest. David Gamut saw Magua take the sisters; (he / she) mounted a horse and followed (her / them).

After the massacre five men walked around the battlefield Colonel Munro and duncan heyward were accompanied by Hawkeye, Chingachgook, and Uncas. After looking for the girls bodys, the men realized they were alive but had been kidnapped.

Review Time!

Edit this passage from *The Last of the Mohicans*.

Hawkeye and his companions succeeded in tracking magua and the girls back to the Huron village. david gamut was outside of the village in the woods, and (he / she) speaked to Hawkeye. The Indians recognized that David was a harmless singer, and they let him come and go as he pleased. He told Hawkeye that Alice was in this village; Cora was in the neighboring delaware village. The Delawares were friends of Hawkeye and the mohicans. Hawkeye did not know why they (was / were) helping Magua.

Duncan decided to accompany David back to the Huron village. He passed (himself / themselves) off as a doctor who wanted to help them. His face paint and wise words satisfied the Indians, who let (he / him) stay Uncas was captured and brought to the Huron village a short while later. Meanwhile, Hawkeye dressed up in a bear skin and also wandered into the huron settlement. with the help of Hawkeye, Duncan managed to find and free Alice. While Hawkeye stayed to help Uncas, Duncan and Alice set off for the nearby Delaware village to join Chingachgook, colonel Munro, and Cora.

Apostrophes

Apostrophes are used in contractions and possessive nouns.

Contractions are two words joined together into a single word. Many contractions are made from pronouns, helping verbs, and the adverb "not." Contractions are formed by replacing a letter or letters with an **apostrophe**.

they are > they're   do not > don't   I am > I'm

The contraction for "will not" changes more than usual.   will not > won't

Apostrophes are also used in **possessive nouns**. Most possessive nouns are formed simply by adding **apostrophe "s"** (**'s**).

dentist's office   Valerie's house   bride's dress

If a noun is **plural and ends with "s,"** just add an **apostrophe** (**'**).

parents' car   sisters' game   kittens' mother

Possessive pronouns do not use apostrophes.

her picture   your desk   my future   their address

Add apostrophes where they belong in the sentences below.

Andrea is here. Shes my best friend. Were going sledding.

Please dont throw that ball inside. Youll break Moms glassware.

I have two dogs. Theyre out in the yard. These are the dogs toys.

He went to the game with Samuels brother. Theyll be home soon.

I wouldnt go in that cave. Its very dark. It might be a bears cave.

Edit this passage from *The Last of the Mohicans*.

David helped Hawkeye, who was still dressed in the bear costume, get in to see uncas. The Hurons had decided that Uncas would be killed in the morning. Hawkeye untied Uncas, and they discussed how (they / them) could escape. David offered to stay behind and pose as Uncas. Hawkeye switched clothes with david, and Uncas put on hawkeyes bear skin. By the time the Hurons discovered the trick, Hawkeye and Uncas (was / were) safe in the Delaware village with the rest of their friends.

The next morning magua went to the Delaware village. He wasnt received well at first, but Magua was very crafty. He gave trinkets and loot to the delaware warriors and made a very flattering speech. The council decided that the prisoners would be given to Magua. Cora throwed herself at the foots of the oldest member of the council and begged for mercy. She said that there was one who hadnt yet spoken. A mark on Uncass chest showed that he was a Mohican. The Delawares had a deep respect for the mohicans, and they rejoiced at seeing Uncas.

Commas

A comma marks a slight pause in a sentence.

Commas are used to separate items in a series.

> She looked under the bed, in the closet, and behind the door.
>
> Travis likes horses, football, and rain.

Commas are used when people are spoken to directly.

> Tomorrow is your birthday, Alex.
>
> Excuse me, Sir, but you are sitting in my seat.

Commas are used to set off an **appositive**, which is a word or phrase that renames the noun(s) or pronoun(s) right before it.

> My grandpa, the man in the overalls, is eighty years old.
>
> We invited the Bradfords, our neighbors, to the party.

Commas are used to set off an interruption in a sentence.

> There are, as you know, only four days left until Christmas.
>
> The winter sale, if I'm not mistaken, was a success.

Add commas where they belong in the sentences below.

Wanda my best friend bakes brownies cookies and bread.

This summer my mother tells me we are going on a vacation.

Will you open the windows Sophie?

My little brother that blonde toddler loves to play outside.

This bus I believe stops in St. Louis Chicago and Milwaukee.

Edit this passage from *The Last of the Mohicans* by adding commas where they belong.

Uncas was brought forward at once, and he spoke on behalf of Hawkeye Cora and Alice. Hawkeye and Alice were freed as well. Uncas was forced however to admit that Cora belonged to Magua according to Indian customs. Magua refused to leave her behind. Hawkeye a brave man offered to take her place, but Magua would not accept the generous offer even though Hawkeye had killed many of Magua's people. Magua and Cora left the Delaware village. Because Magua had come in peace, Indian hospitality declared that he must be allowed to leave in peace.

"I will come after you Magua!" Uncas warned.

Magua only laughed.

Uncas Hawkeye and the Delawares made preparations to go to war with the Hurons. Uncas was in charge. He appointed Hawkeye and other deserving warriors as commanders over the rest. They devised a plan and then split up to carry out the attack. The war in the woods began. The Delaware Indians quickly gained strength and ground.

Review Time!

Edit this passage from *The Last of the Mohicans*.

Uncas and his men pushed the Hurons all the way back to their own village. The huron warriors were quickly falling to the Delaware. Uncas saw Magua and two of his men retreat with Cora. He Hawkeye and Duncan started after them.

Suddenly cora dropped to her knees. (She / Her) refused to go any farther. Magua told her to choose between his wigwam and death, but Cora bravely defied him and wouldnt answer. Magua raised his knife. Before he could strike Cora, Uncas jumped on Maguas back. One of the other Indians stabbed Cora and killed her. Magua struck Uncas with his tomahawk. Before Uncas died, he managed to slay Coras killer. Hawkeye arrived on the scene just as Uncas fell. Magua yelling victoriously was already fleeing. Hawkeye shot (he / him), and Magua dropped to his death.

The next day the delaware indians had a burial ceremony for Cora the beautiful maiden and brave Uncas the last of the Mohicans.

Commas

A comma marks a slight pause in a sentence.

Commas are used to separate two descriptive adjectives unless one or both of them is a color or a number.

> That bright, shiny diamond is very expensive.
>
> That sparkling red ruby is very pretty.

Commas are used after a light exclamation or introductory word beginning a sentence.

> Hey, wait for me!   Embarrassed, I hid behind the bush.

Commas are used after a dependent clause, long prepositional phrase, or two prepositional phrases in a row before the main part of a sentence.

> If you need directions, I can give them to you.

Commas are used to separate two **independent clauses** (complete sentences) joined by a conjunction - AND, BUT, OR, FOR, NOR, SO, YET.

> Brooke was surprised, yet she wasn't scared.
>
> I made supper and set the table, and my brother did the dishes.

Add commas where they belong in the sentences below.

Wow that roller coaster was really fast!

After locking the house I realized I had left my keys inside.

I have a nice red coat but I wore my sister's warm fuzzy jacket.

Yes those energetic spunky ponies are fun to watch.

We are going to the mall and then to the grocery store.

Edit this passage from *The Strange Case of Dr. Jekyll and Mr. Hyde* by adding commas where they belong.

Mr. Utterson and Mr. Richard Enfield went for a walk together every Sunday. The two lived in London and were relatives. On one of these very walks the pair found themselves at a cellar door. It reminded Mr. Enfield of an incident that he had witnessed on that same street. He shared the story with Mr. Utterson.

He had been walking down this street when he had seen a most disturbing thing. A little girl had been running to get the doctor and she had collided with a disfigured man. Instead of helping the girl up the man had trampled right over her and continued on his way. Outraged Mr. Enfield had dragged the man back to the scene, where the girl's family and the doctor had gathered. Rather than calling the police the angry group had demanded that the selfish man pay the girl's family. The man had agreed. He had gone into the cellar door and had come back with a check signed by another man one who was very respectable. Mr. Enfield didn't say who that man was but he did share the name of the rude selfish man.

His name was Mr. Edward Hyde.

Semi-Colons

A semi-colon marks a longer pause in a sentence.

Semi-colons are similar to commas, but a semi-colon marks a longer pause.

Remember that a comma is used when two independent clauses (complete sentences) are joined by a conjunction - AND, BUT, OR, FOR, NOR, YET, SO. If two independent clauses are joined <u>without</u> the use of a conjunction, then a semi-colon is used and there is a longer pause.

> I need to pack my bags tonight, for I am leaving in the morning.
>
> I need to pack my bags tonight; I am leaving in the morning.

Another use for the semi-colon is to separate a series in which there is another series within that already uses commas.

> She painted the living room blue and white; the bedroom white, green, and brown; and the bathroom red.

Add commas and semi-colons where they belong in the sentences below.

You can fold the towels and I will fold the sheets.

This is my room that one belongs to my sister.

My uncle likes spaghetti I prefer lasagna.

Isabelle was tired but did not go to sleep.

The fireman drove away but the policeman stayed at the scene.

Our dog is missing there is a reward for whoever finds him.

I need to go to the post office to mail a letter stop at the store to buy lettuce milk and cheese and run to the bank to cash a check.

Edit this passage from _The Strange Case of Dr. Jekyll and Mr. Hyde_ by adding commas and semi-colons where they belong.

Mr. Utterson a lawyer was very troubled by the story. Although he had never met Mr. Hyde he had heard the name before. One of his friends Dr. Henry Jekyll had given Mr. Utterson his will. In the will Jekyll stated that in the event of his death or disappearance, all of his possessions were to be given to Mr. Hyde. Mr. Utterson hadn't liked the will before he liked it even less after hearing Mr. Enfield's story about Mr. Hyde.

Mr. Utterson was determined to meet Mr. Hyde. He walked by the cellar door many times, waiting in the street to catch a glimpse of the mysterious man. One dreary evening he saw a man unlocking the cellar door. The small man had an evil disfigured appearance. Mr. Utterson disliked him at sight. When Mr. Utterson politely introduced himself Mr. Hyde was very unfriendly. He asked Mr. Utterson how he knew him. Mr. Utterson replied that he had found out from Dr. Jekyll.

The man spat out, "I'm certain he has told you nothing about me!" Mr. Hyde whirled around angrily then he entered the cellar door.

Review Time!

Edit this passage from *The Strange Case of Dr. Jekyll and Mr. Hyde*.

After Mr. Hyde disappeared inside the mysterious door Mr. Utterson decided to visit dr jekyll. His house was right around the corner from the cellar door Mr. Hyde had entered. Mr. Utterson knocked on Dr. Jekyll's door. Poole the butler answered the door and said the doctor was not at home.

As he was leaving, Mr. Utterson realized that the cellar door was actually an entrance to Dr. Jekylls house. The house was arranged in such a way that there appeared to be two separate buildings but they were actually connected. Mr. Utterson couldnt understand how Dr. Jekyll could be friends with the evil Mr. Hyde. He came to the conclusion that edward hyde was blackmailing Dr. Jekyll for some unknown reason.

Two weeks later Mr. Utterson had the chance to talk to Dr. Jekyll. He decided to be honest he told the doctor he was worried about his friendship with Mr. Hyde. Dr. Jekyll told the lawyer not to be worried. He said he could be rid of Mr Hyde at any time.

Quotes

A quote is the exact words of a speaker.

If someone says something directly, it is a **quote**.   "I have a dog," Barry said.

If someone else tells us what they said, it's not a quote.   Barry said he has a dog.

Quotes are marked with **quotation marks**. They go around the speaker's words.

The first word of a quote is capitalized even if it is not the beginning of the sentence.

    Barry said, "<u>M</u>y dog knows a lot of tricks. He can shake hands."

If the quote is split, as shown in the example below, there are quotation marks at the

beginning and end of each part of the quote. Don't capitalize the beginning of the

second part of the quote unless it is the start of a new sentence.

    "I think," Barry stated, "that my dog is the best dog in the world."

Unless there is an exclamation point or question mark, use a comma to separate the

quote from the speaker's name. All punctuation goes inside the quotation marks.

    Barry continued<u>,</u> "My dog has even won a dog show."

    "My dog's name is Floyd<u>,</u>" Barry said.

    "I lost my dog<u>!</u>" Barry yelled. "Have you seen him?"

Add capital letters and punctuation to the sentences below.

my father said to sweep the driveway and rake the yard

happy birthday aunt sadie shouted how old are you now

i think mr schutt said it's going to rain

what's for supper i asked.   leftovers my mom replied

Edit this passage from *The Strange Case of Dr. Jekyll and Mr. Hyde*.

Almost a year later a terrible crime was committed in london. Sir Danvers Carew a highly-respected man was murdered. A maid happened to see the whole thing from her window. The murderer was a man she had seen before. She was certain that it was Mr Hyde!

Mr. Utterson took the police to Mr. Hydes house. The house was completely ransacked. There were clothes strewn about and evidence of burned papers. The police also found part of a cane, which was the murder weapon. Mr. Hyde (was / were) gone.

Mr. Utterson went to Dr. Jekyll's house that same day. He was worried that Mr. Hyde might be after Dr. Jekyll too.

i have no idea where Mr. Hyde is Dr. Jekyll said. we (is / are) no longer friends.

Dr. Jekyll also said that he had received a letter from Mr. Hyde. He showed the letter to Mr. Utterson. It said that mr. hyde was grateful for Dr. Jekyll's kindness and that (he / him) had left London.

Edit this passage from *The Strange Case of Dr. Jekyll and Mr. Hyde*.

Time passed, and still Mr. Hyde was not captured. With the absence of the evil man, Dr. Jekyll became a new person. He became very sociable involved himself in charitable work and invited friends over often. Mr. Utterson was glad to see that Mr. Hydes influence over Dr. Jekyll had disappeared along with the man himself.

One day Mr. Utterson went to visit dr Jekyll. Poole answered the door and said that the doctor didn't want any visitors. Although Mr. Utterson returned many times the butler always informed him that Dr. Jekyll didnt want to see anyone. He had shut himself up in his room.

Mr. Utterson decided to visit Dr. Lanyon another friend of his and Dr. Jekyll's. When Mr. Utterson arrived, he was surprised to see that Dr. Lanyon looked terribly ill! the doctor explained that he had suffered a terrible shock and didn't think he would recover. He refused to talk about Dr. Jekyll at all.

One week later Dr. Lanyon died. He leaved a letter for Mr. Utterson but the lawyer was not to open it until the death or disappearance of Dr. Jekyll.

Edit this passage from *The Strange Case of Dr. Jekyll and Mr. Hyde*.

Mr. Utterson and mr. enfield were out for another one of their sunday walks. They passed by Dr. Jekyll's house. Mr. Utterson saw his friend sitting by one of the windows. He called out a greeting, which Dr. Jekyll returned. Then Dr. Jekyll's smile changed into a look of horrible suffering and he quickly turned away from the window. The two men were very disturbed they agreed not to speak about what they had seen.

Some time later Poole came to see Mr. Utterson. He was worried about his master.

I'm afraid that something bad has happened to Dr. Jekyll Poole began.

Like what Mr. Utterson asked.

Please Mr. Utterson come back to the house with me. I want to show you something Poole replied.

Mr. Utterson agreed to go back to Dr. Jekylls house with the butler.

Midterm

Edit this passage from *The Strange Case of Dr. Jekyll and Mr. Hyde*.

Poole explained that Dr. Jekyll had shut himself up eight days ago and hadnt come out since. he knocked on the door and told Dr. Jekyll that Mr. Utterson had come to see him. The weak angry voice that called back (was / were) not Dr. Jekyll's. This was what poole had wanted Mr. Utterson to see for himself. Poole thinked that someone had killed dr. jekyll and was still in the room! He had worked for Dr. Jekyll for twenty years he knew that the voice did not belong to his master.

Mr. Utterson and Poole decided to break into the room. It was the only way to know if Dr Jekyll was still alive. They began to break through the door with an axe. they heard a scream of terror. Then there was quiet. When they made it through the door, they saw the body of edward hyde. He had killed himself before they could question (he / him). They looked all over for Dr. Jekyll but he was nowhere to be found. He had disappeared

Mr. Utterson finded a letter with his own name on it on the table.

Adjectives

Adjectives are words that describe nouns and pronouns.

Adjectives describe nouns and pronouns. **Possessives** function as adjectives.

It took me <u>six</u> minutes to ride <u>my</u> <u>shiny</u> <u>red</u> bicycle to <u>Ben's</u> house.

Adjectives are used to compare nouns and pronouns.

My <u>older</u> sister has <u>good</u> ideas, but my <u>oldest</u> sister has <u>better</u> ideas.

Proper adjectives are formed from proper nouns and are capitalized.

Our <u>Tennessee</u> home has <u>French</u> doors.

Predicate adjectives come after a linking verb.   That bread looks <u>fresh</u>.

Articles "a," "an," and "the" are adjectives.   <u>An</u> owl and <u>a</u> bat live in <u>the</u> barn.

Demonstrative adjectives are like demonstrative pronouns, but they are adjectives when they <u>do</u> name the noun.   <u>These</u> toys belong on <u>that</u> shelf.

Indefinite adjectives are like indefinite pronouns, but they are adjectives when they <u>do</u> name the noun.   <u>Each</u> student had <u>some</u> questions.

Circle all of the adjectives in the sentences below.

Josie dug a big hole in the soft dirt, but Ryan's hole was bigger.

Many people enjoy the unique sound of Irish music.

That flock of wild geese is louder than a busy street.

On vacation this year, we spent several days at a California beach.

Read this passage from *The Strange Case of Dr. Jekyll and Mr. Hyde*. Circle as many adjectives as you can find.

Mr. Utterson left Dr. Jekyll's messy house and returned to his own. Now that Dr. Jekyll had disappeared, Mr. Utterson could read the mysterious letter Dr. Lanyon had left behind.

The letter explained the disturbing event that had shocked the doctor. One evening Dr. Lanyon had received an urgent letter from Dr. Henry Jekyll. It said that he was in trouble and needed Dr. Lanyon's help. Dr. Jekyll wanted Dr. Lanyon to go to his London house and bring back a little drawer, which contained a certain fluid and some powder. Someone would then come to Dr. Lanyon's house to get them. Dr. Lanyon had done as Henry Jekyll had asked. That same night a small, evil-looking man had come to the door and asked for those items. When Dr. Lanyon had given him the liquid and powder, the ugly man had mixed them together and drank them. Then, right before Dr. Lanyon's eyes, the man had transformed into Dr. Jekyll!

Edit this passage from *The Strange Case of Dr. Jekyll and Mr. Hyde*.

After reading Dr. Lanyon's letter, mr Utterson opened the letter from Henry Jekyll It explained everything that had happened.

Dr. Jekyll had been very interested in the two different person-alities he recognized in (himself / themselves). The first was his "good" person the doctor who was respected by his friends and did charitable deeds. The second was his "evil" personality, whose secret thoughts and desires Dr. Jekyll had simply tried to hide and ignore. he had beginned trying to separate the two personalities. By drinking a certain chemical concoction, he had one night actually transformed into his "evil" self, which he named edward hyde. Whereas most people are a mixture of good and evil, Edward Hyde (was / were) pure evil. Because this personality had been ignored for so long Edward Hyde was much smaller and weaker than Dr. Jekyll.

Dr. Jekyll drinked the concoction whenever he felt like releasing his evil side. Disguised as Edward Hyde, he was free to do whatever he wanted. Then he could drink the liquid to turn back into Dr. Jekyll and Mr. Hyde would simply disappear.

Edit this passage from *The Strange Case of Dr. Jekyll and Mr. Hyde*.

Dr. Jekylls evil nature had gradually gained strength. Then one day Dr. Jekyll had turned into Mr. hyde just by thinking an evil thought! He was so startled by this transformation that he vowed never to release his evil side again. However the desire built up inside of him until one day he again became Edward Hyde. The rage had become so great that Mr. Hyde had killed sir danvers carew that same night. Dr. Jekyll had no choice but to banish Edward Hyde forever for he was now a criminal and could no longer show his face freely.

For two months Dr. Jekyll was back to his normal self. Then Edward Hyde breaked through again. He had become too strong to be ignored. Dr. Jekyll was forced to keep himself shut up in his house. He no longer had control. Whenever he went to sleep or had a weak moment, he became Mr Hyde. During one of his last periods as Dr. Jekyll he had written a new will leaving everything to Mr. Utterson. When Poole and Mr. Utterson had come to check on (he / him), he had killed himself. It was the only way to get rid of the evil Mr. Hyde.

Edit this passage from *A Tale of Two Cities*.

It was the year 1775. Crime was rampant in england, and the common people of france were suffering from extreme poverty. The rulers and nobles of France however lived in great comfort and riches. They were unsympathetic to the peasants in their country, and they lived lavishly with no regard for their poor countrymen.

A man from London Mr. Lorry was traveling to Paris. He was a loyal employee of tellson's bank, which had branches in both paris and london. A young woman, Miss Lucie Manette, joined him in Dover. She had been told that Mr. Lorry had information regarding her father, who had died before her birth.

Indeed Mr. Lorry had some difficult news. Her father was not dead he had been in prison for eighteen years on false charges. He had recently been released and was in the care of one of his former servants. Mr. Lorry offered to accompany Lucie and miss pross, Lucie's guardian, on their journey to find Dr. Manette and bring him home to London.

Adverbs

Adverbs are words that describe verbs, adjectives, and other adverbs.

Adverbs are similar to adjectives. However, adjectives describe nouns and pronouns, and adverbs describe verbs, adjectives, and other adverbs. Many adverbs end in **"-ly."**

Andy does <u>not</u> work <u>slowly</u>. (Adverbs "not" and "slowly" describing verbs)

His job is <u>really</u> boring.   (Adverb "really" describing adjective "boring")

Andy works <u>very</u> <u>quickly</u>.   (Adverb "very" describing adverb "quickly")

Adverbs describe four basic things - **time**, **place**, **manner**, and **degree**.

Andy works <u>tomorrow</u>. (time)   Andy works <u>inside</u>. (place)

Andy works <u>tirelessly</u>. (manner)   Andy <u>always</u> works. (degree)

Adverbs are also used to compare. For **comparative adverbs**, add **"-er"** to most one-syllable adverbs and use **more / less** before most two-or-more-syllable adverbs. For **superlative adverbs**, add **"-est"** to most one-syllable adverbs and use **most / least** before most two-or-more-syllable adverbs. **Irregular adverbs** change form completely.

I marched <u>slowly</u>. My friend marched <u>slower</u> than I did.

Of all the ballerinas, that one dances <u>least</u> <u>gracefully</u>.

She sews <u>well</u>, but my mother sews <u>better</u>.

Complete the sentences below by writing adverbs in the blanks.

I run _____.   She talks _____.

This is _____ dirty.   He snores _____.

Ruth walks clumsily. I walk _____ than she does.

He plays badly, but I play even _____ .

Read this passage from *A Tale of Two Cities*. Circle as many adverbs as you can find.

Mr. Lorry was an old acquaintance of Lucie's father. He was the one who had graciously taken little Lucie to England when her mother had died many years before.

Lucie and her companions finally arrived at the Defarge's wine shop, where Lucie's father was living. Mr. Defarge had been a servant of Dr. Manette's in the past. He was now letting the doctor stay in one of his rooms. Mr. Lorry and Lucie followed Mr. Defarge inside. When they entered Dr. Manette's room, they saw an old man sitting upright at a workbench. The man was diligently making shoes. He did not recognize Mr. Lorry, and he referred to himself simply as "One Hundred and Five, North Tower." He was very startled by Lucie's presence, and he spoke of how she reminded him of his wife.

Lucie spoke to her father tenderly and promised to take care of him.

Edit this passage from *A Tale of Two Cities*.

five years later Lucie and her father (was / were) living a pleasant life in london. Dr. Manette had come back to his senses under his daughter's faithful tender care. The Manettes were in a courtroom, where Charles Darnay a Frenchman was being tried for treason. Executions were common in England in those days and Darnay was expected to be found guilty. He was charged with conspiring to help the french king in wars against England.

Several witnessis were called to testify. The first John Barsad repeated the accusations against Darnay and said that he had seen him with a list of names of english soldiers. Incidentally Lucie had also seen and spoken with Charles Darnay five years ago on a ship bound from Paris to England. She testified that she had seen him talking with other frenchmen and passing papers back and forth, but she didn't know what the papers said or what the conversations were about. She said that she hoped her words would not harm the prisoner for he had been very kind to her and her father.

Edit this passage from *A Tale of Two Cities*.

Another witness was called to the stand. He claimed that he had seen darnay traveling and gathering information. The witness insisted that the man he had seen was definitely the prisoner. Darnay's lawyer Mr. Stryver pointed to another man and asked him to remove his wig. When the man did so, the crowd was stunned. He looked just like Charles Darnay This coincidence weakened the last witness's testimony enough to get the prisoner released. Lucie Dr. Manette Mr. Stryver and Mr. Lorry gathered around Charles Darnay and congratulated him.

That evening Mr. Stryver was sitting in his office with mr Sydney Carton, the man who looked like Charles Darnay. Mr. Stryver was a successful lawyer; Mr. Carton served simply as the lawyers clerk. Mr. Stryver believed Sydney could be successful if he applied himself but Sydney argued that he was too prone to drinking and would never be a good man. He blamed it simply on natural rank.

Mr. Lorry, Mr. Stryver, Mr. Carton, and Mr. Darnay became good friends of the manettes and visited them regularly.

Edit this passage from *A Tale of Two Cities*.

in France a man known as Monsieur the Marquis was traveling home to his chateau. He had been at a party with other rich well-to-do citizens. Like the others, Monsieur the Marquis did not work but he lived richly and oppressed the peasants. He cared nothing for their welfare and felt no guilt about his lifestyle. The peasants meanwhile were becoming angrier every day over their intense oppression.

charles darnay was the nephew of Monsieur the Marquis. He visited his uncle, and they argued. Charles hated the way the nobles lived, but his uncle only cared about his own comforts. Charles told his uncle that he was going to live in england and work for his money. He did not want to live in France and bear the shame of his familys wickedness. That was why he had changed his name and left france.

That night Monsieur the Marquis (was / were) murdered by a peasant!

Prepositions

Prepositions add meaning to sentences by showing time,
location, direction, or how two things are related to one another.

Prepositions begin **prepositional phrases**. This phrase includes all of the words from the preposition up to a noun(s) or pronoun(s), which is the **object of the preposition**. The preposition shows how the object relates to another word in the sentence.

She placed the milk <u>inside the refrigerator</u>.

A preposition is always followed by an object (a noun or pronoun). If there is no object, the word is most likely an adverb.   She took the milk <u>inside</u>.

Prepositional phrases can function as adjectives or adverbs. **Adjectival phrases** tell what kind or which one and modify nouns and pronouns. **Adverbial phrases** tell how, when, or where and modify verbs, adjectives, and adverbs.

That boy <u>with the blonde hair</u> lives <u>by the lake</u>.
 adjectival - which one   adverbial - where

Rose tells stories <u>with surprise endings</u> <u>in a dramatic tone</u>.
 adjectival - what kind   adverbial - how

Underline the prepositional phrases. Identify them as adjectival or adverbial.

I got a letter from my grandma.   _____

My friend looked around.   _____

She walked with purpose.   _____

The path winds through the garden.   _____

Kitchens with oak cabinets are nice.   _____

Read this passage from *A Tale of Two Cities*. Underline the prepositional phrases and circle the objects of the prepositions.

Another year passed. Charles Darnay became a French tutor in England. He fell in love with Lucie, and he shared his feelings with her father. Dr. Manette approved of the match.

Charles was not the only one who loved the beautiful girl. Sydney Carton also loved her, and he told her so one night. He said he knew she could never love someone of his character, but he wanted to tell her that she had affected him in a way he had never thought possible. He told Lucie that he loved her enough to give his life to keep someone she loved beside her. Sydney asked her not to tell anyone about their conversation, and he said he would never mention it again.

Some time later Charles and Lucie were married. On the morning of their wedding day, Charles told Dr. Manette his real name and who he was. Dr. Manette promised to keep his secret.

Charles and Lucie continued to live with Dr. Manette. They had a beautiful daughter, and they named her Lucie. They lived many happy years together in England.

Edit this passage from *A Tale of Two Cities*. Identify the underlined prepositional phrases as adjectival (adj.) or adverbial (adv.).

Meanwhile, the country of France was in turmoil. Mr and Mrs Defarge, who lived just outside <u>of Paris</u>, were among the many disgruntled peasants. Their wine shop had been a meeting place <u>for the oppressed poor</u> to gather and share information for many years. While Mr. Defarge was committed to their cause Mrs. Defarge was far more determined. By 1789 the peasants had reached their boiling point. Led by the defarges, (they / them) stormed the Bastille a french prison. They killed the prison officers and released their fellow countrymen.

Within three years the peasants ruled france. The nobility had all either been killed or imprisoned or had fled <u>from the country</u>. Instead of restoring peace, the peasants continued <u>in their rage</u>. Their fight against oppression took an ugly turn. They (was / were) now imprisoning and executing innocent people without giving them fair trials. large numbers of people were killed each day by the angry mob <u>of peasants</u>.

Edit this passage from *A Tale of Two Cities*.

    With all of the turmoil in France, the paris branch of tellson's bank was a mess. In 1792 Mr. Lorry was called upon to travel to Paris on business. On the night he left Charles Darnay was visiting him. Mr. Lorry had a letter for marquis st. everemonde of France, and Charles Darnay offered to deliver it. Only Charles and Dr. Manette knew that Charles was actually the Marquis of St. Everemonde.

    The letter was from a man who was a servant to Charles Darnay. He had been put in prison by the peasants because he worked for nobility. Charles felt that he had no choice but to go to Paris and help his faithful servant. He knew that France had become a dangerous place but he did not know just how bad it was. Charles wrote a letter to Lucie and a letter to Dr Manette. He hoped to spare them some pain by leaving before they knew what he was doing. Then he left for paris. He thought that the peasants would respect (he / him) because he had turned his back on his title and was coming back of his own free will.

Edit this passage from *A Tale of Two Cities*.

Charles was arrested as soon as he arrived in Paris. the peasants had passed new laws and given themselves the power to imprison others.

Dr. Manette Lucie her daughter and miss pross traveled to Paris as soon as they learned about Charles's arrest. Dr. Manette was convinced that he could help Charles. Because he himself had been wronged by the nobles and imprisoned falsely for many years he was accepted by the peasants as one of their own. However he was unable to use his power to get Charles released. Charles was held in prison for over a year, but lucie and her father still had hope that he would be freed. Many others were being executed every day. They were lucky that Charles was still alive.

Finally the peasants set a date for Charles's trial On the day of the trial it was revealed that Charles had been imprisoned based on the charges of three different people. The three who had denounced Charles were Mr. Defarge Madame Defarge and Dr. Manette

Direct and Indirect Objects

Direct objects receive the action of the verb.

Indirect objects are the receivers of some direct objects.

A **direct object** is the noun or pronoun that directly receives the action of the verb.

To identify the direct object, ask *what* or *whom* received the action.

Natasha caught the <u>football</u>.   The girl chose <u>me</u>.

What did Natasha catch? The <u>football</u>.   Whom did the girl choose? <u>Me</u>.

Some sentences may have **compound** (more than one) direct objects.

We brought <u>hamburgers</u>, <u>hotdogs</u>, and <u>chips</u> to the picnic.

Some sentences with direct objects also have **indirect objects**. An indirect object names the person (or thing) *to whom* or *for whom* something was done.

My friends threw <u>me</u> a party.

What did they throw? A <u>party</u>. For whom was the party thrown? <u>Me</u>.

There may also be compound indirect objects.

Grandma gave <u>me</u> and my <u>sister</u> a new game.

What was given? A <u>game</u>. To whom was it given? <u>Me</u> and my <u>sister</u>.

Identify any direct objects (DO) or indirect objects (IO) in the sentences below.

The doctor examined Ethan's knee.

My friend told me a secret.

Juan bought his mother and father a present.

She baked her family some cookies.

Edit this passage from *A Tale of Two Cities*. Identify any direct or indirect objects in the underlined sentences.

Dr. Manette instantly denied the statement. However, mr. defarge had a letter that Dr. Manette had wrote while he was in prison. In the letter Dr Manette told the story of how he had been arrested. Many years ago, two brothers who (was / were) noble-men had come to the doctor for help. They showed him a young woman and her brother. Both were dying. Dr. Manette learned that the brothers had taken the peasant girl from her family. When her brother came to rescue her, they had wounded (he / him) with a sword. Dr. Manette (was / were) deeply troubled. Before he could report the matter Dr. Manette had been kidnapped by the brothers and thrown in jail. At the end of the letter, Dr. Manette denounced the brothers and their families. Little did he know that one of the brothers had a son who would grow up to be an honest man. That man was Charles Darnay, who was now married to Dr. Manettes own daughter

The peasant girl and boy mentioned in the letter were the brother and sister of madame defarge. That was why the Defarges had denounced Charles and had him arrested.

Edit this passage from *A Tale of Two Cities.*

The peasants were outraged by the crimes detailed in the letter. They decided that Charles Darnay would be executed the very next day for the suffering his family had caused the peasants. dr. manette could do no more for his son-in-law.

Meanwhile Sydney Carton arrived in paris He met with Mr. Lorry and gave him clear instructions to take the manette family back to London the next day. Sydney had found John Barsad the man who had testified against Charles Darnay at his first trial. He knew the spy had been lying and he threatened to report him. John Barsad agreed to help Sydney get in to the prison to see Charles.

The next day, just two hours before Charles was to be executed, Sydney went to visit him. He traded clothes with Charles, and then he caused him to faint. John Barsad took Charles who was disguised as Sydney to Mr. Lorry and the Manettes. Sydney was executed in Charles's place. He died in peace, knowing that it was a gooder thing than he had ever done before. He knowed that lucie would remember his words, "to keep someone she loved beside her."

Edit this passage from *The Merry Adventures of Robin Hood.*

By the time Robin Hood was just a young man he could shoot an arrow more skillfully than any other man. In robin hood's eighteenth year, the Sheriff of Nottingham announced that he was holding a shooting contest. Robin Hood set off from his own town of locksley towards nottingham to participate in the contest. On his way Robin Hood came upon fifteen men. Seeing the youth with his bow and arrows, the men began to tease him. No young man likes to be teased about his manhood, and Robin Hood quickly challenged the loudest man to a shooting contest. Robin Hood winned fair and square the man refused to pay him. Instead he shot an arrow at Robin Hood. Robin Hood sent one back. The man dropped down dead and Robin Hood fled into sherwood forest. He felt sick and full of sorrow for his actions.

Robin Hood was now an outlaw! He remained hidden in Sherwood Forest for he could no longer live in town. The sheriff offered two hundred pounds for his capture.

Edit this passage from *The Merry Adventures of Robin Hood*.

In the first year that Robin Hood lived in sherwood forest many other mans came to join him. These men were good honest men who fled to the forest for one of two main reasons. Some of them were wanted for killing the kings deer. The law stated that the deer belonged to the king and anyone caught shooting one was arrested. It didn't matter how poor or hungry or desperate they were. The second reason men came to join Robin Hood was that they had been made poor by the dishonest and oppressive rulers. Many of the barons abbots knights and other officials imposed high taxes and unfair fines on the common people.

Robin Hood's band of outlaws growed to around a hundred in number. The common people learned to love them Robin Hood and his merry men took the wealth away from those who were oppressing the poor and returned it to the needy. No one who came to robin hood for help was turned away.

Confusing Words

Some words are often confused with similar words.

Here are some tips to help you remember which word to use when:

good - good is an adjective
This is a <u>good</u> meal.

well - well is an adverb
You cook very <u>well</u>.

can - use can to show ability
I <u>can</u> run very fast.

may - use may to ask permission
<u>May</u> I run in the race next week?

than - used to make comparisons
She laughed harder <u>than</u> I did.

then - tells when
<u>Then</u> she cried.

real   - genuine or authentic
This desk is a <u>real</u> antique.

really - an adverb meaning "very"
It is <u>really</u> old.

affect - a verb meaning "to influence"
The rain <u>affected</u> our picnic plans.

effect - a noun meaning "result"
The <u>effect</u> was that we ate inside.

who's   - the contraction of "who is"
<u>Who's</u> going to the shoe store?

whose - a possessive pronoun
<u>Whose</u> shoes are these?

Circle the correct words in the sentences below.

This is a (good / well) movie. I like it better (than / then) that one.

Do you know (who's / whose) scarf this is? It is (real / really) warm.

(Can / May) I see that stuffed toy? It looks like a (real / really) animal.

He told the story (good / well). It had an inspiring (affect / effect) on us.

66

Edit this passage from *The Merry Adventures of Robin Hood.*

One day Robin Hood came to a (real / really) narrow bridge. just as he began to cross, a tall stranger started crossing from the other side. The bridge was not wide enough for two men. After arguing about (who's / whose) duty it was to step aside they decided they would fight with their staffs until one of them knocked the other into the water. They struggled for over an hour before the tall man finally succeeded in knocking robin hood into the stream. Robin Hood congratulated the stranger. The stranger had fought (good / well), and Robin Hood was very impressed by his skill. (Than / Then) Robin Hood asked the man to join his band of merry men. The strangers name was john little. He was at least seven feet tall and he was wider (than / then) any man Robin Hood had ever met. The merry men renamed the newcomer Little John. He became Robin Hood's right-hand man and most close friend.

Little John was not the only man Robin Hood recruited. Whenever Robin Hood came upon a likable skilled man, he asked (him / them) to join his band of merry men and share in their adventures.

Edit this passage from *The Merry Adventures of Robin Hood.*

The Sheriff of Nottingham had not forgotten about Robin Hood. After a few different attempts to catch him, he comed up with a (real / really) clever plan. He decided to hold a shooting contest and offer a prize that Robin Hood couldnt resist. He knew Robin Hood would want to prove his skill.

On the day of the shooting match the sheriff of nottingham didn't see Robin Hood anywhere. The contest continued until only the three best archers were left. These three were Gilbert Adam and an unknown beggar. The crowd cheered loudly for Gilbert and Adam but the beggar won. The sheriff congratulated the beggar and gave him a golden arrow.

i declare he said, you shoot gooder than Robin Hood, (who's / whose) too much of a coward to even show his face!

That evening the Sheriff of Nottingham was feasting when an arrow flyed through the window. A scroll was attached. It read, "Today you gave a golden arrow not to a beggar, but to none other (then / than) Robin Hood."

Edit this passage from *The Merry Adventures of Robin Hood.*

The Sheriff of Nottingham was very angry that Robin Hood had outsmarted him. He tried many times to capture the outlaw but it seemed that robin hood was simply too clever. As for Robin Hood, he decided to teach the sheriff a lesson.

Nearly a year after the shooting match, Robin Hood set off towards nottingham. He met a butcher and bought his clothes meat and cart. Robin Hood dressed up in the butcher's clothes and went to Nottingham to sell the meat. He selled it very cheaply to the poor and the widows.

After he'd sold all of the meat Robin Hood saw the Sheriff of Nottingham. Robin Hood invited him to a feast The sheriff didn't recognize Robin Hood and followed him willingly. Robin Hood took him to sherwood forest to his band of merry men. Then he took off his disguise. The sheriff was angry but could do nothing. After sharing a grand feast with his guest, Robin Hood took the sheriffs ill-gotten money and sent him on his way.

Edit this passage from *The Merry Adventures of Robin Hood.*

some time later Robin Hood sended out six of his men. (They / Them) needed a rich man to come and feast with them in order to get more money. The men returned with a guest but he was not wealthy. He was a minstrel, and he was deeply distraught. His name was allan dale. He was in love with a beautiful maiden who loved him in return. However, the girl's father had pledged her to an old knight. they were to be married in just two days.

Robin Hood vowed to help. Taking a handful of men, he set off to find a holy man. He came into the company of Friar Tuck, who agreed to help. On the morning of the wedding, they went to the church. When Robin Hood approached the old knight he humbly stepped aside. The maidens father however was not as easy to persuade. As Robin Hood had brought Friar Tuck to marry the couple, the father was left with no choice. Robin Hood paid him (good / well) to give his blessing anyway.

Allan Dale and friar tuck both joined robin's band of merry men.

Modifiers

Modifiers provide additional information about the words they modify.

Modifiers have to be placed correctly for clear meaning. If a modifier is modifying the wrong word or it is unclear which word in the sentence it is modifying, it is called a **misplaced modifier**. A modifier is a **dangling modifier** if its subject isn't included in the sentence at all or when its intended subject isn't the actual subject of the sentence.

Here is an example of a misplaced modifier. The sentence is very confusing.

The glass fell off the counter <u>filled with milk</u>.   The counter was filled with milk?

The glass <u>filled with milk</u> fell off the counter.   This sentence is clear.

Here is an example of a dangling modifier. The subject is not what was intended.

<u>Crossing the street</u>, the traffic was heavy.   Subject seems to be "traffic."

<u>Crossing the street</u>, I noted the heavy traffic.   Correct. "I" is now the subject.

Rewrite the sentences below so that the meanings are clear.

I put a flower in my hair, which smelled very good.

Walking underneath the tree, my umbrella ripped.

She noticed a girl standing by the fence with a ponytail.

Dad handed me a present with a big smile.

His neck was stiff after counting all of the stars in the sky.

Edit this passage from *The Merry Adventures of Robin Hood*. Find and underline one misplaced modifier and one dangling modifier.

One fine autumn day Robin Hood and Little John set off in
different directions. They were trying to find a guest to share their
feast that was rich. Robin Hood met a knight but he was not rich.
In fact, he was deeply in debt. His name was Sir Richard, and he
told Robin Hood his story. Sir Richards son had been involved in a
jousting accident now Sir Richard was being forced to sell his lands
and everything he had to keep his son out of prison.

Little John on the other hand brought the Bishop of Hereford,
who was very wealthy. After the merry men feasted with their two
guests, Robin Hood collected payment from the bishop. He took
one third for the band gave one third to Sir Richard and returned
the other third to the bishop.

Sir Richard was very grateful to Robin Hood and his men. Vowing
to repay Robin Hood, the money was counted carefully. The next
year true to his word sir richard came back to sherwood forest
and paid back every penny he had borrowed.

Edit this passage from *The Merry Adventures of Robin Hood.*

Robin hood and his merry men were enjoying the cool shade of Sherwood Forest when a visitor arrived. It was none other than the queen's page, and he came bearing an important invitation from queen Eleanor herself King Henry was holding a shooting match and the queen wanted Robin Hood and some of his men to come. Robin Hood choosed Little John Will Scarlet and Allan Dale to accompany him.

King Henry didnt know that Queen Eleanor had invited Robin Hood. On the day of the competition, she made a bet with the king. She bet that she could find three men who could beat the king's goodest three archers. The king agreed to the wager.

When the best three archers were left from the king's men, the queen called out Robin Hood and his friends. The king was very surprised to see the outlaws but (he / him) had given the queen his word.

Edit this passage from *The Merry Adventures of Robin Hood.*

Six new targets were bringed out for the competition between the king's archers and the outlaws. Will Scarlet shot against Hubert of suffolk for third place. Although Will shot very well Hubert won the round. The king smiled at the queen the queen smiled back.

Little John was competing against tepus for second place. Two of Tepus's arrows hit the center, but all three of Little Johns found the middle of the target.

Lastly Robin Hood faced gilbert to see who would win first place. Gilbert shot first and hit the middle circle with all three of his arrows. It was the best shooting the crowd had seen all day. The king was confident that he would win the bet However, Robin Hood shot his three arrows so close to the center of the target that they looked like a single arrow!

Taking first and second prize, robin hood and his men were declared the winners of the competition. Queen Eleanor won the bet

Edit this passage from *The Merry Adventures of Robin Hood*.

Many months had passed since the shooting match. King Henry had died, and king richard now sat on the throne. Robin Hood and his band of merry men continued to hunt feast and seek adventure.

The Sheriff of Nottingham had realized that he couldn't capture Robin Hood himself but he still wanted him catched. The sheriff hired a notorious outlaw Guy of Gisbourne to find and kill Robin Hood. The two met one day in the forest. They had never seen each other before, and Guy didnt know that he was speaking to robin hood. Guy introduced himself and told Robin Hood why he had come. At this Robin Hood revealed his identity. They drew their swords. After a long vicious fight, Robin Hood killed his opponent. Although Robin Hood took no satisfaction in his victory, he knew guy had been a terrible man responsible for many deaths.

Robin Hood disguised himself as Guy of gisbourne and rescued Little John, who had been caught by the sheriff that same day.

Labeling Sentences

There are many different parts of speech, including subjects, verbs, adjectives, adverbs, prepositions and prepositional phrases, and direct and indirect objects. Here is a quick review:

The subject is who or what the sentence is about.

The verb tells the action of the subject or provides more information. There are action, linking, and helping verbs.

Adjectives modify nouns and pronouns.

Adverbs modify verbs, adjectives, and other adverbs.

Prepositions begin prepositional phrases, which end with a noun or pronoun.

The direct object receives the action of the verb.
The indirect object is the receiver of the direct object.

In the sentences below, underline the subjects once and the verbs twice. Circle the adjectives. Mark the adverbs (ADV), the direct objects (DO), and the indirect objects (IO). Cross out any prepositional phrases.

Joshua spotted nearly a dozen tadpoles in the pond.

Mom passed me the warm French bread and soft butter.

After supper Ruth carefully painted a picture of a brilliant sunset.

The snowman by our sidewalk did not melt very quickly.

Edit this passage from *The Merry Adventures of Robin Hood.*

Now king Richard had heard about Robin Hood and his merry men and he very much wanted to meet them. He was impressed by the storys he had heard about their kindness. He and six of his men disguised (himself / themselves) as friars and journeyed to sherwood forest. They counted on Robin Hood and his men inviting them into the forest for a feast, and that was exactly what happened.

When the feast was over Robin Hood demanded the usual hefty payment from their guests. The king lifted his hood. Robin Hood and his men kneeled at once. King Richard spoke to the band. He asked them to come into his royal service. He invited Robin Hood Little John Will Scarlet and Allan Dale to accompany him back to london. The rest of the men could stay in the forest as royal rangers. All of them (was / were) pardoned for their crimes!

Robin Hood and his men heartily agreed to the king's terms. The Sheriff of nottingham was vexed indeed when the king returned home with robin hood at his side!

Edit this passage from *Twenty Thousand Leagues Under the Sea.*

It was the year 1866 when ships first began to report strange sightings of a mysterious object in the seas. Although at first these reports were scoffed at and dismissed it soon became clear that it did exist. Numerous ships recorded sightings and even collisions with the unknown form. The mysterious object was widely discussed. all rumors and gossip aside, there were two possible explanations. Either the object was an unknown sea monster of incredible size and speed, or it was a man-made submarine built better (than / then) any other known vessel.

I Pierre Aronnax arrived in new york just as these events were unfolding. As the assistant professor at the museum of natural history in paris, I had spent six months conducting a scientific expedition in nebraska. Because of my reputation as an expert marine biologist my opinion was widely requested. After reviewing the facts, i published an article stating my position. I believed that the mysterious monster was a narwhal of enormous size and power.

Edit this passage from *Twenty Thousand Leagues Under the Sea.*

The majority of the general public agreed with my assessment. After one particular ship was badly damaged by the mysterious menace, it was clear that the creature must be found and killed. The american government took action at once. A man named commander farragut was chosen to lead the hunting expedition. A fast frigate the *Abraham Lincoln* was loaded with all kinds of guns cannons and harpoons.

As I was in new york at the time of the ships departure, I was asked to join the expedition. I had been looking forward to returning home to France but i could not turn down this unique opportunity. I left immediately for the ship with my faithful servant and companion Conseil.

Commander Farragut and his crew were determined to kill the giant narwhal. Among the men on the ship was a canadian named Ned Land. He was a skilled harpooner, and he was confident in his abilities. However he was one of the only men on the ship who didn't believe that such an animal existed.

Edit this passage from *Twenty Thousand Leagues Under the Sea*.

A reward of two thousand dollars was offered by Commander Farragut to the first man to spot the monster. Everyone on board the *abraham lincoln* kept a careful watch on the seas, but three months passed without a sighting. Just before we gived up Ned Land spotted the creature.

It was a short distance from our ship and it was glowing. It was at least two hundred and fifty feet long and shot water over a hundred feet into the air. We pursued the monster for nearly a day with no success. It possessed remarkable speed and maneuverability. That night we got close enough for ned to try and spear it. He hurled his harpoon at the creature, but it bounced off the hard surface with a loud clang.

The creature shot water over our ship. I tumbled into the cold black water below. When i made it back up to the surface, the *Abraham Lincoln* was too far away for me to signal. Just as I began to sink a strong hand pulled me back to the surface. It was Conseil my trustworthy companion. He had seen me fall overboard and had jumped in after (I / me).

Diagramming Sentences

Sentence diagrams show how the words relate to each other.

A **sentence diagram** is a visual picture of a sentence. The subject and verb go on the main line separated by a vertical line. Predicate nouns or adjectives (those which come after a linking verb) go after the verb, separated by a diagonal line.

| Grant | smiled |

| He | was \ late |

Adjectives and adverbs go on slanted lines beneath the words they modify.

Prepositional phrases also go beneath the words they modify. The preposition goes on a slanted line, which leads to the object of the preposition on a new horizontal line.

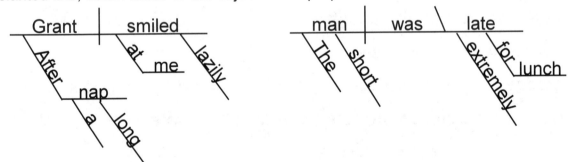

Diagram the sentences below.

Some of the clouds were very dark.

The young girl fell down the flight of stairs.

A brilliant rainbow appeared in the sky above our heads.

These Georgia beaches are beautiful in the early spring.

My cousin on my mother's side swam across the dirty river.

Edit this passage from *Twenty Thousand Leagues Under the Sea.*

Conseil was as calm as always. While one of us floated on his back the other one swam and drove (we / us) forward. We took turns to conserve our strength until we could be rescued. We kept up this routine for nearly two hours. Just as my strength gave out, conseils cry of help was answered. He continued to push us forward. Much to our surprise, it was ned land who had called to us. He had also been swept overboard he was now stranded on the back of the monster.

Ned helped us onto the floating object, and I began to inspect the surface. I realized that i had been wrong about the monster. It wasn't a narwhal after all. It was a man-made vessel of steel and we were sitting on top of it. The moment it dived back under the water, we would all be lost!

Just then an iron panel opened Eight men appeared. They dragged us into the vessel and left us in a dark chamber. (We / Us) had no choice but to sit and await our fate.

Edit this passage from _Twenty Thousand Leagues Under the Sea._

A short while later two men came to visit us. They turned on a light and spoke in an unintelligible language. I explained who we were in french and english but they made no response. Conseil tried german without any result. The men left the room, and a silent steward brought us supper. The food was exquisite. After eating our fill, we fell asleep. The next day one of the same men came to visit us again.

  professor aronnax will you join me he asked. He spoke in perfect french.

  My companions and i were shocked The man continued to speak. He informed us that we were his prisoners, and he had decided to let us live. However we would never be allowed to leave the submarine. his existence under the sea was unknown, and he wanted to keep it that way. We had no choice but to accept his decision. He introduced himself as captain nemo and (than / then) again invited me to join him. The captain was well-acquainted with both my name and my work.

Edit this passage from *Twenty Thousand Leagues Under the Sea.*

Captain Nemo gave me a complete tour of his craft the *nautilus*. The large submarine was actually a very luxurious vessel with a dining room library drawing room and comfortable living quarters. The rooms were extremely well-furnished with tasteful furniture and expensive works of art. Captain Nemo was clearly a very rich man.

The captain also explained to me how the *Nautilus* was capable of such speed and agility. It was powered by electricity. While i had only heard of small amounts of power being generated in this way, the captain had figured out a way to generate much larger amounts. He was obviously a very smart well-educated man as well. Captain Nemo showed me a variety of instruments some familiar and some unknown which helped guide the *Nautilus*. It rose to the surface each day to renew its oxygen supply. A small boat affixed to the top of the craft enabled the captain to take short fishing or pleasure trips.

In this fashion captain nemo and his crew traversed the globe explored the oceans depths and collected fascinating specimens.

Edit this passage from *Twenty Thousand Leagues Under the Sea*.

Despite being prisoners we enjoyed a comfortable life on the *nautilus*. Our meals consisted of excellent fare provided by the ocean and cooked to perfection by captain Nemos chef. The library offered hundreds of volumes for us to read. A huge window in the drawing room gave (we / us) a captivating view of the ocean and the abundant life therein. When we surfaced we (was / were) allowed to stand on top of the vessel and breathe the fresh air. on occasion Captain Nemo invited us to explore the ocean's floor with him. We weared special suits complete with breathing devices. I was able to study the depths of the sea like never before.

Captain Nemo was a strange man. We enjoyed a certain level of companionship and shared a mutual feeling of respect. Some days i spent many hours talking with and learning from Captain Nemo other times I didnt see him for long periods of time. For unknown reasons, the captain had abandoned the world of mans and preferred to live free from rules and laws under the ocean.

Sentence Combining

Sometimes it is helpful to combine two or more short sentences into one longer sentence.

Instead of using several short, choppy sentences, sometimes two or more thoughts can be combined into one sentence.

I saw a bear cub. It was brown. The bear cub was by a tree. Its mother was with him.

These four sentences can easily be combined into a single sentence.

I saw a brown bear cub and its mother by a tree.

Combine each group of sentences below into one sentence.

I play baseball. I am on a Little League team. I play third base.

Nathan is building a fort. The fort is in a tree. Marcus is helping Nathan. They are almost finished.

Brenda made cookies. They are sugar cookies. There are four dozen.

I have to wrap a present. It is for my sister. It is her Christmas present.

Our neighbors have three dogs. They also have two cats. There are five kids in the family. Our neighbors live in a big house. It is gray.

We have two fruit trees. They are in our backyard. They are cherry trees.

Edit this passage from *Twenty Thousand Leagues Under the Sea.*

We spent many months exploring oceans gulfs and seas all over the world. I was enthralled by the experience and began writing notes for a new book on marine life. This unique lifestyle afforded me the opportunity to indulge in my personal passion. Conseil was content as always just to be close by my side. He appreciated the wonderful sights nearly as much as I did. ned land, however, grew weary of life on the submarine. He was a hunter by trade and was tired of being confined under the water. His temper worsened each week and he was determined to escape as soon as possible.

Although I was enjoying our journey I agreed that we should escape if we ever got the chance. It was clear that captain nemo was never going to free us, and I very much wanted to return with my notes to my homeland and family. Our only hope was that we would journey close enough to a civilized country. we would steal the small boat and paddle as far as we could. Hopefully a ship would spot us and come to our rescue.

Edit this passage from *Twenty Thousand Leagues Under the Sea.*

We had been on the *nautilus* for over four months. during that time we had saw many new and wonderful sights. We (was / were) currently heading for the south pole. I was amazed at the captain's sense of adventure.

The *Nautilus* moved along the surface of the water. When we reached the Great Ice Barrier, i thought that our adventure would have to be forsaken. The captain however was determined to be the first to reach the South Pole. He proposed that we go under the ice. We would fill the submarines reservoirs with oxygen so that we could stay underwater longer.

Over a day and a half later we rose to the surface and took our bearings. We had reached the South Pole Captain Nemo planted his flag.

On our way back, a mountain of ice fell into the ocean, blocking our path. We were trapped Working in shifts, we used picks to chip away at the ice. It took us days and our oxygen reserve was quickly depleted. By the time we broke through and rose to the surface we had all nearly suffocated.

Edit this passage from *Twenty Thousand Leagues Under the Sea.*

a couple of months later we had another deadly experience. Ned Land Conseil and I (was / were) looking out the window when we comed upon a group of giant cuttlefish. The ugly squid-like creatures were well over twenty feet long and had eight enormous arms covered with hundreds of suction cups. They were angered by our presence.

The *nautilus* stopped with a sudden shock. Captain Nemo entered the drawing room with a somber look on his face. A cuttle-fish had got tangled up with the submarine. We had no choice but to rise to the surface and fight the monstrous creature in order to regain control. each man was armed with an axe; Ned Land chose a harpoon. As soon as the panel was opened the cuttlefish thrust two of its giant arms into the vessel. It grabbed the closest seaman and dragged him out of the ship. Captain nemo let out an angry yell he began to attack the disgusting creature with his hatchet. An intense battle followed. We defeated the cuttlefish but we were unable to save the unfortunate seaman.

Final Examination

Edit this passage from *Twenty Thousand Leagues Under the Sea.*

Captain Nemo wept at the loss of his crew member He retreated to his room and I didnt see him for many days. The *Nautilus* wandered about with no set course.

After ten months on board the *nautilus* ned was desperate to escape. One day he told me that we were going to escape that very night. He had gone on top of the vessel that morning when it had surfaced he had spotted land about twenty miles away. Whether we made it or not, we agreed that it (was / were) worth the risk.

We were in the process of detaching the small boat that night when we heard a loud cry. The *Nautilus* was heading into a giant whirlpool No ship had ever escaped from this powerful force. Our hearts seemed to stop in terror. My head striked something hard and I sank into darkness.

When I woke up, i was lying in the house of a fisherman. Ned Land and conseil were sitting beside me. Our survival was a mystery. An even greatest mystery was the fate of captain nemo and his extraordinary *Nautilus*.

Complete Sentences

...ify run-ons or fragments. In the others, underline the complete ...ject once and complete predicate twice. Circle each simple ...ject and simple predicate.

...e large barn cats. (fragment)

...a picture of a giant snake.

...four sisters played a card game.

...lives in California he likes swimming in the ocean and sand ...yball. (run-on)

...thin brown curtains fluttered in the cool breeze.

...ried up an old oak tree. (fragment)

...crickets chirped all day and all night.

1

Read this passage from *Around the World in Eighty Days*. Identify any run-on sentences. Make sure each underlined sentence is complete. If it is, circle the simple subject and the simple predicate. If it is not, identify the fragment as a subject (s) or a predicate (p).

Phileas Fogg lived in London in 1872. Resided in a house on Saville Row with just one servant.(p) Phileas Fogg was a member of the esteemed Reform Club. Beyond that, very little was known about him. He was rich, for sure, but no one knew how he had become wealthy. He seemed to be very knowledgeable about other countries and cultures, but no one could remember him leaving London in many years.

One day Phileas Fogg.(s) He had a very exact, punctual nature. His daily routine was followed to the minute, without any variance in his activities. He spent a good part of each day at the Reform Club where he read newspapers and ate fine meals and played whist a card game of which he was very fond. (run-on)

Because Phileas Fogg spent so much time at the Reform Club, his servant had very little to do. However, Phileas expected his man to be extraordinarily exact. On October 2, 1872, Phileas dismissed his present servant. Had brought Phileas shaving water two degrees too cold.(p)

2

Sentence Types

...sometimes possible to end a sentence more than one way. The most ...mon confusion is whether to use a period or an exclamation point. In ...n instances either one can be used with only a slight change in ...ing. For this reason, it is not "wrong" if students use periods in place ...clamation points or vice versa, unless the sentence obviously requires ...r the other. If this ever happens, simply take the opportunity to discuss ...ossibilities and decide which would be more effective.

...capital letters and ending punctuation to the sentences below. ...ify the type of each one.

...o bed.	imperative
...urse was stolen!	exclamatory
...do you like your eggs?	interrogative
...the cabinet.	imperative
...house has a big basement.	declarative
...ou scared of the dark?	interrogative
...barn is on fire!	exclamatory

3

Edit this passage from *Around the World in Eighty Days* by adding capital letters and ending punctuation where needed. Use all three types of ending punctuation.

There are 10 errors in this passage.

That same morning a Frenchman by the name of Passepartout came to apply for a job. Passepartout was looking for a quiet life as a servant. He knew that Phileas Fogg was a man with an exact routine, and he was pleased when Phileas hired him.

At exactly half past eleven, Phileas Fogg left for the Reform Club as he did every day. Passepartout found a card outlining the details of his master's routine and the daily duties expected of the servant.

That night Phileas Fogg played whist with his usual partners. Their conversation revolved around a recent bank robbery. The thief had stolen fifty-five thousand pounds! Phileas's friends began to argue about the chances of the man being caught. Fogg remarked that it was now possible to go around the world in only eighty days. This started a new argument, which ended with Phileas betting twenty thousand pounds on his remark. His friends accepted. Phileas Fogg stated that he would return to the club in exactly eighty days, on Saturday, December 21, 1872.

Passepartout was shocked! What had happened to his quiet life?

4

Review Time!

Edit this passage from *Around the World in Eighty Days*. Underline any sentence fragments and identify them as subjects (s) or predicates (p).

There are 9 errors in this passage.

T̲he remarkable wager of Phileas Fogg quickly spread throughout the Reform Club and all of England. People chose sides and made wagers of their own with their friends. Most people bet against Fogg, especially after a certain telegram was received in London. I̲t said that Detective Fix of the Scotland Yard had found the bank robber and was following him. The robber's name was Phileas Fogg!

Put a stop to the betting.(p) People began to talk about the strange habits of Phileas Fogg. His mysterious ways seemed suspicious. T̲hey thought he'd made the wager simply to escape. Detective Fix had seen Phileas Fogg and Passepartout in Egypt. He had been on the wharf when they arrived by ship. Phileas fit the description of the bank robber, and Detective Fix was convinced from the first moment that he was indeed the thief. H̲e sent a telegram to the police in London asking them to send a warrant to Bombay. He planned to follow Phileas to Bombay, get the warrant, and arrest him at once!

5

Nouns

Sometimes words like "Mom" and "Dad" may take the place of a name. For example, in the sentence "M̲other wrote a letter," *Mother* is capitalized because it is used in place of a name - "C̲allie wrote a letter." However, the sentence "M̲y mother wrote a letter," it is not capitalized because you would not put a name there - "M̲y Callie wrote a letter."

Titles used with names are capitalized - "A̲unt C̲allie."

Identify the nouns in the first column as common or proper. Identify the nouns in the second column as concrete or abstract.

restaurant	common	relaxation	abstract
Speckles	proper	whisper	concrete
Hawaii	proper	wisdom	abstract
grandparents	common	money	concrete
rose	common	rose	concrete
year	common	scent	concrete
World War I	proper	opportunity	abstract

6

Read this passage from *Around the World in Eighty Days*. Circle at least fifteen common nouns. Underline and capitalize the proper nouns.

F̲ix befriended P̲assepartout in order to find out more about the mysterious P̲hileas F̲ogg. P̲assepartout was completely unaware of the detective's schemes and was only too happy to find a friend.

The ship to B̲ombay, I̲ndia arrived two days early. P̲hileas F̲ogg recorded the fact in his notebook and calmly went to the passport office to get his passport marked. D̲etective F̲ix went to the police, where he learned that the warrant had not yet arrived.

P̲hileas, P̲assepartout, and S̲ir F̲rances C̲romarty, a fellow passenger from the ship, took the train from B̲ombay to C̲alcutta. However, the rails had not quite been completed, and the passengers were forced to find another source of transportation. P̲assepartout thought that this delay would ruin them, but P̲hileas was not put out in the least. He found a man with a trained elephant and bought it for two thousand pounds - an extraordinary amount! P̲assepartout was speechless. P̲hileas hired an elephant driver and kindly invited S̲ir F̲rances C̲romarty to join them.

7

Capitalization

Point out to students that small, unimportant words like "the," "a," and "o" titles are not usually capitalized unless they are the first word of the title.

Add capital letters and periods where they belong in the sentences below.

O̲n S̲aturday my dad and I̲ are going to an I̲llinois football game.
S̲he got a D̲ell computer for C̲hristmas.
N̲ext J̲anuary our family is going on a C̲aribbean cruise.
O̲ur neighbor, L̲ieut. J̲. H̲arrison, owns four G̲erman shepherds.
A̲unt J̲anice is coming to visit on the third W̲ednesday in M̲arch.
S̲he introduced herself as M̲rs. P̲atricia M̲. J̲ackson.
B̲efore I̲ went to bed, I̲ read two chapters in my book.

8

92

this passage from *Around the World in Eighty Days*.

are 18 errors in this passage.

elephant driver knew the <u>C</u>alcutta countryside well and was
rmined to make the trip as quickly as possible. However, late
aturday afternoon they heard something. It was a <u>B</u>rahmin
al procession. They hid amongst the trees and watched the
mins pass. Some of them were leading a beautiful young
an, who kept trying to break away. When the <u>B</u>rahmins had
peared from sight, their guide told them what was happening.
young woman had been forced to marry a rajah. He had died,
now the <u>B</u>rahmins were going to sacrifice her at his funeral!
Phileas <u>F</u>ogg simply suggested, "Let's save her."
ssepartout and <u>S</u>ir <u>F</u>rances agreed. They waited until night, but
uards did not go to sleep. In the early morning the funeral
ed. Phileas <u>F</u>ogg was just about to run into the crowd when the
le all fell facedown. The dead rajah had risen up, taken his
in his arms, and was walking away<u>!</u>
en the rajah came closer, <u>P</u>hileas recognized <u>P</u>assepartout.
ad daringly snuck in to the camp to rescue the unconscious
g woman! They quickly boarded the elephant and set off,
wly avoiding capture.

9

Review Time!

Edit this passage from *Around the World in Eighty Days*.

There are 20 errors in this passage.

The young woman's name was <u>A</u>ouda, and she was quite
charming. She was the daughter of a rich merchant and had
received an <u>E</u>nglish education. She spoke English very well and
was extremely grateful to her rescuers. She agreed to accompany
them to <u>H</u>ong <u>K</u>ong, where she had a relative who would take care
of her.
When they reached their destination, <u>P</u>hileas gave the elephant to
the driver, who had proved most faithful.
<u>D</u>et<u>.</u> <u>F</u>ix was waiting for Phileas in <u>C</u>alcutta. He was again unable
to detain him, so he continued to follow him. He boarded the same
ship, which would take the passengers from <u>I</u>ndia to <u>H</u>ong <u>K</u>ong<u>.</u>
Passepartout saw the detective on the ship, and he became
suspicious. He decided that <u>F</u>ix had been sent by the members of
the <u>R</u>eform <u>C</u>lub to make sure Phileas Fogg actually went around
the world.
Due to the stormy <u>O</u>ctober weather, the steamship arrived a day
late. Therefore, <u>P</u>hileas <u>F</u>ogg missed the ship to <u>J</u>apan.

10

Plural Nouns

the nouns below. Write the plural forms in the blanks provided.

h	<u>crutches</u>	child	<u>children</u>	calf	<u>calves</u>
	<u>deer</u>	library	<u>libraries</u>	engine	<u>engines</u>
	<u>dishes</u>	mouse	<u>mice</u>	camera	<u>cameras</u>
	<u>chefs</u>	man	<u>men</u>	mess	<u>messes</u>

11

Edit this passage from *Around the World in Eighty Days*. **Cross out
any misspelled plural nouns and write the correct plural nouns above.**

There are 18 errors in this passage.

As it turned out, Aouda's relative had left Hong Kong and was now
living with some other [families] in <u>H</u>olland. Phileas Fogg invited
<u>A</u>ouda to travel back to <u>E</u>urope with them, and she was delighted.
She had grown quite attached to <u>M</u>r<u>.</u> <u>P</u>hileas <u>F</u>ogg, and her eyes lit
up with respect and love for him. Phileas seemed unaware of her
affection, but he made sure she was as comfortable as possible and
that her few [wishes] were met.
The travelers went through a series of adventures after landing in
Hong Kong<u>.</u> The long and short of it was that despite getting
separated for a while, Phileas, Aouda, Passepartout, and <u>D</u>etective
<u>F</u>ix all managed to board a steamship bound for <u>C</u>alifornia.
Detective Fix had to wait until Phileas Fogg was back on <u>E</u>nglish
soil in order to arrest him. He told <u>P</u>assepartout who he really was.
Passepartout was outraged<u>!</u> However, Detective Fix explained that
he now wanted Phileas to make it back to <u>L</u>ondon as quickly as
possible, and the two became [allies].

12

93

Verbs

Circle all of the verbs in the sentences below. Identify them as action (a), linking (l), or helping (h) verbs.

My cousin may arrive two days early. (helping, action)

Dad looked funny in the top hat. (linking)

We were very content. (linking)

She was arranging the flowers in a vase. (helping, action)

The whale splashed everyone in the front row. (action)

Dr. Wise will be performing the surgery. (helping, helping, action)

13

Read this passage from *Around the World in Eighty Days*. Identify underlined verbs as action (a), helping (h), or linking (l) verbs.

Phileas Fogg and company were(h) traveling(a) by train to New York. In Nebraska, Indians attacked(a) the train. The conductor was left unconscious, and the train was(h) traveling(a) at a very high speed. If it couldn't be stopped at the Fort Kearney station, all would be lost!

When Passepartout heard this, he slipped(a) underneath the train. He carefully crawled from car to car until he reached the engine. He managed to unhook it, and it continued on alone while the rest of the train slowed(a) to a stop just short of the Fort Kearney station. When the passengers were counted, three of them were missing, including Passepartout. Despite the fact that the next train wouldn't wait, Phileas led(a) a band of thirty men to find the missing passengers. He was(l) determined to find them.

After a successful rescue mission, Phileas returned(a) to the Fort Kearney station. Phileas, Passepartout, Aouda, and Fix boarded a unique vehicle called a sledge, which would(h) whisk(a) them all to Omaha in enough time to catch the next train. Thankfully, the rest of the journey to New York passed without excitement.

14

Review Time!

Edit this passage from *Around the World in Eighty Days*.

There are 13 errors in this passage.

When Phileas Fogg reached New York, he learned that he had missed the steamship to England by just forty-five minutes! While the rest of the group began to complain, Phileas set off right away to find out which [countries] other ships were going to. He found a ship bound for France. He and the others boarded the steamer.

The next day the captain was outraged to find the ship on a course to England! Phileas Fogg had paid the crew to take him to England. The captain was powerless and angry, but Phileas calmed him by buying the ship for much more than it was worth.

Phileas arrived in England on the 21st before noon. The group sat down to their [lunches]. Phileas had more than enough time to make it to London. Just then Detective Fix put a hand on Phileas's shoulder.

"You're under arrest," Detective Fix said, and he took Phileas to prison.

Nearly two hours later Det. Fix rushed in to see Phileas Fogg.

"I'm sorry!" he yelled, "You're free! The robber was found three days ago!"

15

Verb Tenses

Identify the complete tense of each verb/verb phrase underlined below.

She shall have raked the yard. _____future perfect_____

The twins raced to the playhouse. _____simple past_____

I will be sewing a dress for the play. _____future progressive_____

They had walked home from the park. _____past perfect_____

Seth is cleaning up the mess. _____present progressive_____

16

94

this passage from *Around the World in Eighty Days*. Identify the
plete tense of each underlined verb/verb phrase.

leas Fogg and his friends boarded (simple past) a train and
towards London. When they stepped off the train, the clocks
 striking (past progressive) ten minutes before nine. Phileas
just five minutes late!

 next evening Phileas told Aouda he was sorry he had brought
 perfect) her to England, as he was now poor. Aouda asked
as to marry her. She had grown to love him and did not care
he was poor now. Phileas loved Aouda in return, so he sent
epartout to the reverend's house.

ssepartout came rushing back. He grabbed Phileas and said,
it is (simple present) not Sunday! It's Saturday! You must go
e Reform Club! You will have won (future perfect) the bet!"

leas had made a mistake! By traveling continually eastward,
ad gained an entire day. He thought he had arrived (past
ect) in London on Saturday night at ten to nine, but it had been
y night at ten to nine!

 rushed to the Reform Club, and at precisely 8:45 on Saturday,
ember 21, he was standing (past progressive) before his
nished whist partners. He won the bet and received (simple
 twenty thousand pounds.

leas Fogg had made it around the world in eighty days!

17

Irregular Verbs

Students probably know and use most irregular verbs already. However,
some of them might be a little tricky. To familiarize students with irregular
verbs, use a basic framework for them to repeat the verb in the present
tense, past tense, and past participle. For example, with the irregular verb
"speak," the student would say "Today I speak; yesterday I spoke; yesterday
I had spoken." Reading the sentence out loud often helps students remember or recognize the correct form of the verb.

Write the past tense and past participle of each present tense verb.
(blow) Yesterday I __blew__ a bubble.   I had __blown__ a bubble.
(fall)   Yesterday I __fell__ down.   I had __fallen__ down.
(give)   Yesterday I __gave__ a dime.   I had __given__ a dime.
(see)   Yesterday I __saw__ a deer.   I had __seen__ a deer.
(take)   Yesterday I __took__ a bath.   I had __taken__ a bath.

18

---

this passage from *The Last of the Mohicans*. Cross out any
rect irregular verbs and write the correct verbs above.

 are 7 incorrect irregular verbs in this passage.

 French and English were fighting for control of North America.
colonists [fought] with the English; many of the Indian tribes
t with the French. Colonel Munro was the commander of Fort
am Henry, one of the English forts. He [sent] a letter to
eral Webb, the commander of Fort Edward, asking him to bring
orcements immediately. The French army, under the command
ontcalm, was advancing toward Fort William Henry. Munro
w] he would need more men for the upcoming battle.
nro's beautiful daughters, Cora and Alice, were also at Fort
ard. They were leaving for Fort William Henry to join their
r. Major Duncan Heyward [rode] along with them as their
dian. Another man, David Gamut, was also traveling with them.
sang] Psalms. The little party was being [led] by an Indian
r, Magua. He was a friend to the English and [took] the group
rt William Henry by way of a shortcut through the woods.

19

Review Time!

Edit this passage from *The Last of the Mohicans*.
There are 15 errors in this passage.

 Just two miles west, two men [sat] and talked. One of them was
a white man, although his face was sunburned and worn as though
he spent a lot of time outdoors. He was dressed ruggedly and
carried a rifle and a knife. His name was Hawkeye, and he was a
scout. He had lived with the Indians for most of his life. The man
he was talking with was an Indian named Chingachgook. Hawkeye
and Chingachgook were great friends, closer than brothers.

 Chingachgook had a son named Uncas. They were the last of
their people, the Mohicans. The three [men] had been living and
hunting together for a long time. Uncas joined his father and
Hawkeye, and they [began] to eat supper.

 Meanwhile, the small party of travelers [came] close to where the
three men were eating. Duncan asked the scout if they were near
Fort William Henry. Hawkeye replied that they were going in the
wrong direction. When Hawkeye saw Magua, he recognized him as
a Huron. Hawkeye [told] Duncan that the Hurons were a thievish
people and could not be trusted. The men tried to catch Magua,
but he escaped into the woods.

20

Subject / Verb Agreement

It may help students to read the sentences out loud.

Circle the correct verbs in the sentences below.

They (**walk** / walks) everyday. He (walk / **walks**) faster than she does.

My brother (**is** / am) tired. I (is / **am**) tired too.

Neither Mom nor my aunts (**cook** / cooks) supper on Fridays.

Do you (**throw** / throws) very far? She (throw / **throws**) really far.

Libby (**clean** / cleans) her room often. I never (**clean** / cleans) mine.

I (is / **am** / are) leaving. (Is / **Am** / Are) you going with me?

21

Edit this passage from *The Last of the Mohicans*. Circle the correct verbs.

There are 9 errors in this passage.

When Duncan Heyward realized that they had been deceived betrayed by Magua, he didn't know what to do. He (**was** / were) responsible for the safety of the two sisters. He asked Hawkeye and his companions for help. After a short discussion, Hawkeye announced that they were willing to lead the party to Fort William Henry.

Hawkeye, Chingachgook, and Uncas (was / **were**) capable, trustworthy, and caring. Knowing that Magua would return with more Hurons, they led their new friends to a secret hiding place. It was cave with hidden entrances surrounded by waterfalls.

For a while the group was able to rest. However, soon the Hurons returned. The men fought well, but eventually Hawkeye, Chingachgook, and Uncas [knew] that they would be overcome. There was nothing to do now but hide in the cave. Although the brave men were prepared to fight to the death, Cora urged them try and escape.

"If you (**escape** / escapes)," she said, "you can send help for If Magua (**capture** / captures) all of us, there will be no hope of being rescued!"

22

Verbals

Identify the types of verbals underlined in the sentences below.

I gave the <u>sleeping</u> baby to his mother.   <u>participle</u>

<u>Bowling</u> is one of my favorite sports.   <u>gerund</u>

My mom wants <u>to read</u> all of the classics.   <u>infinitive</u>

<u>To live</u> in medieval times would have been exciting.   <u>infinitive</u>

The group of <u>smiling</u> customers left a nice tip.   <u>participle</u>

I started <u>skiing</u> two years ago.   <u>gerund</u>

23

96

Read this passage from *The Last of the Mohicans*. Identify the underlined verbals as gerunds (g), infinitives (i), or participles (p).

Although they didn't want <u>to leave</u>(i), Hawkeye and the Mohicans realized that Cora was right. <u>Escaping</u>(g) was their only chance They dropped into the swirling water and disappeared from sight Cora tried to convince Duncan to follow them, but he refused to leave the girls. Instead, Duncan and Cora did their best to calm <u>crying</u>(p) Alice. She was very frightened and shook uncontrollably

The four travelers hid as deep in the cave as they could, but eventually Magua and the Hurons found them. They dragged them out of the cave. Cora and Alice were put on <u>rested</u>(p) horses, while Duncan and David were made to walk. They did not know what the Hurons planned <u>to do</u>(i) with them.

When they stopped for a meal, Cora bravely approached Magua. She asked him to release Alice and pour out his anger on herself. <u>Asking</u>(g) was not easy! Magua replied that he would let Alice go Cora would consent <u>to be</u>(i) his wife and live in his wigwam. Cora was disgusted by the offer. She told Duncan and Alice what he said. In a moment of strength, Alice replied that it would be better for them to die together.

24

Review Time!

this passage from *The Last of the Mohicans*. **Identify the**
rlined verbals as gerunds (g), infinitives (i), or participles (p).

e are 11 errors in this passage.

en Cora refused Magua's offer, he announced that they would
e killed. One of the Indians approached Alice. Duncan angrily
ed on him, but the Indian (was / were) too strong. Just before
Huron could sink his knife into Duncan, the sound of a rifle
ed through the woods. The Indian fell down dead. Hawkeye,
gachgook, and Uncas charged into the camp! Fighting(g)
e out immediately. Only Magua managed to escape(i), wounded
live. The three warriors explained that after escaping down
ver, they had hidden nearby. Uncas had [found] the fleeing(p)
ns' trail, and they had followed them, waiting for a chance to
e the group.
ough there were both Huron and French [enemies] between
and Fort William Henry, Hawkeye and his companions (was /
) able to escort(i) the group safely to the fort. Colonel Munro
delighted to be reunited with his daughters. Duncan Heyward
also glad to be back. He wanted to ask the colonel for
ission to marry Alice!

25

Pronouns

Circle all of the pronouns in the sentences below.

Simon drove himself home. Someone went with him. Who was it?

Those are very noisy. They are singing. Both are too loud.

Abigail went to bed. She was tired. I am tired myself.

We are late. No one was ready. Whom should we apologize to?

26

---

this passage from *The Last of the Mohicans*. **Circle the correct**
ouns.

e are 10 errors in this passage.

ough Munro was overjoyed by the presence of his daughters,
as not well. (They / Them) were under attack from the
ch, and so far no help had arrived from Fort Edward.
onel Munro met with the leader of the French army, Montcalm.
French had captured a messenger on his way to Fort William
y. Montcalm showed a letter to Colonel Munro. It (was /
) from General Webb, and it said that (he / him) was not
ing reinforcements. He advised Colonel Munro to surrender
ontcalm.
nro was prepared to fight bravely to the end, but Montcalm
ed him a peaceful compromise. The English had to leave the
out Montcalm would allow (they / them) to take their arms and
s with them. In this way the English army would maintain their
ty, and both [armies] would be spared unnecessary bloodshed.

27

Pronoun / Antecedent Agreement

Circle the correct pronouns in the sentences below.

My uncle and cousin are coming. (He / They) are coming today.

I am building a shelf. (I / Me) am building it all by (itself / myself).

The class starts in the fall. (It / They) lasts for three months.

He took the dogs for a walk. (It / They) love going for walks.

Isaac grilled some hotdogs. (He / She) ate (it / them) all.

28

Edit this passage from *The Last of the Mohicans*. Circle the correct pronouns.

There are 11 errors in this passage.

   While the <u>F</u>rench were satisfied with the agreement, their <u>I</u>ndian allies were not. They had expected to be rewarded with loot from those they killed in the fighting. This new arrangement didn't offer (him / them) the opportunity to gain anything.

   The Indians waited as the <u>E</u>nglish army moved away from the fort. They watched with greedy eyes. Cora noticed <u>M</u>agua moving amongst (they / them). Suddenly the Indians began ripping clothing and other trinkets away from the English. Magua let out a piercing war cry, and the attack began in earnest. Dozens of [women], [children], and soldiers (was / were) killed. Magua recognized Cora and Alice. He put them on horses and led them into the forest. David Gamut saw Magua take the sisters; (he / she) mounted a horse and followed (her / them).

   After the massacre five men walked around the battlefield. Colonel Munro and <u>D</u>uncan <u>H</u>eyward were accompanied by Hawkeye, Chingachgook, and Uncas. After looking for the girls' [bodies], the men realized they were alive but had been kidnapped.

29

Edit this passage from *The Last of the Mohicans*.

There are 11 errors in this passage.

   Hawkeye and his companions succeeded in tracking <u>M</u>agua an the girls back to the Huron village. <u>D</u>avid <u>G</u>amut was outside of village in the woods, and (he / she) [spoke] to Hawkeye. The Indians recognized that David was a harmless singer, and they him come and go as he pleased. He [told] Hawkeye that Alice in this village; Cora was in the neighboring <u>D</u>elaware village. Th Delawares were friends of Hawkeye and the <u>M</u>ohicans. Hawke did not know why they (was / were) helping Magua.

   Duncan decided to accompany David back to the Huron village He passed (himself / themselves) off as a doctor who wanted help them. His face paint and wise words satisfied the Indians, let (he / him) stay. Uncas was captured and brought to the Hu village a short while later. Meanwhile, Hawkeye dressed up in bear skin and also wandered into the <u>H</u>uron settlement. <u>W</u>ith th help of Hawkeye, Duncan managed to find and free Alice. Whil Hawkeye stayed to help Uncas, Duncan and Alice set off for the nearby Delaware village to join Chingachgook, <u>C</u>olonel Munro, Cora.

30

Apostrophes

   Possessives ending with "s" can be tricky. If a singular noun ends with an "s" or a "z" sound, you may just add an apostrophe. However, there is one exception. If a singular noun ending with "s" is a one-syllable word, it requires both an apostrophe and "s." **That is <u>Russ's</u> boot.**

Add apostrophes where they belong in the sentences below.
Andrea is here. She's my best friend. We're going sledding.
Please don't throw that ball inside. You'll break Mom's glassware.
I have two dogs. They're out in the yard. These are the dogs' toys.
He went to the game with Samuel's brother. They'll be home soon.
I wouldn't go in that cave. It's very dark. It might be a bear's cave.

31

Edit this passage from *The Last of the Mohicans*.

There are 12 errors in this passage.

   David helped Hawkeye, who was still dressed in the bear costume, get in to see <u>U</u>ncas. The Hurons had decided that Ur would be killed in the morning. Hawkeye untied Uncas, and the discussed how (they / them) could escape. David offered to s behind and pose as Uncas. Hawkeye switched clothes with <u>Da</u> and Uncas put on <u>H</u>awkeye's bear skin. By the time the Huron discovered the trick, Hawkeye and Uncas (was / were) safe in Delaware village with the rest of their friends.

   The next morning <u>M</u>agua went to the Delaware village. He wa received well at first, but Magua was very crafty. He gave trinke and loot to the <u>D</u>elaware warriors and made a very flattering speech. The council decided that the prisoners would be given Magua. Cora [threw] herself at the [feet] of the oldest member the council and begged for mercy. She said that there was one hadn't yet spoken. A mark on Uncas's chest showed that he w Mohican. The Delawares had a deep respect for the <u>M</u>ohicans they rejoiced at seeing Uncas.

32

98

Commas

...he first rule, using commas in a series, students are taught to use

...as after each item. However, students may notice some writers omit

...st comma (before "and"). This is not technically wrong, but it is

...ming more and more common to use a comma here. It also helps

... the sentence clearer, so it is a good habit for students to learn.

...asize to students that commas are not needed if all of the words in

...es are connected by the word "and."

...commas where they belong in the sentences below.

...da, my best friend, bakes brownies, cookies, and bread.

...summer, my mother tells me, we are going on a vacation.

...you open the windows, Sophie?

...ttle brother, that blonde toddler, loves to play outside.

...bus, I believe, stops in St. Louis, Chicago, and Milwaukee.

33

Edit this passage from *The Last of the Mohicans* by adding commas where they belong.

There are 9 errors in this passage.

Uncas was brought forward at once, and he spoke on behalf of Hawkeye, Cora, and Alice. Hawkeye and Alice were freed as well. Uncas was forced, however, to admit that Cora belonged to Magua according to Indian customs. Magua refused to leave her behind. Hawkeye, a brave man, offered to take her place, but Magua would not accept the generous offer even though Hawkeye had killed many of Magua's people. Magua and Cora left the Delaware village. Because Magua had come in peace, Indian hospitality declared that he must be allowed to leave in peace.

"I will come after you, Magua!" Uncas warned.

Magua only laughed.

Uncas, Hawkeye, and the Delawares made preparations to go to war with the Hurons. Uncas was in charge. He appointed Hawkeye and other deserving warriors as commanders over the rest. They devised a plan and then split up to carry out the attack. The war in the woods began. The Delaware Indians quickly gained strength and ground.

34

Review Time!

...his passage from *The Last of the Mohicans*.

... are 14 errors in this passage.

...cas and his men pushed the Hurons all the way back to their

...village. The Huron warriors were quickly falling to the

...ware. Uncas saw Magua and two of his men retreat with Cora.

...Hawkeye, and Duncan started after them.

...denly Cora dropped to her knees. (She / Her) refused to go

...arther. Magua told her to choose between his wigwam and

...h, but Cora bravely defied him and wouldn't answer. Magua

...d his knife. Before he could strike Cora, Uncas jumped on

...ua's back. One of the other Indians stabbed Cora and killed

... Magua struck Uncas with his tomahawk. Before Uncas died,

...anaged to slay Cora's killer. Hawkeye arrived on the scene

...s Uncas fell. Magua, yelling victoriously, was already fleeing.

...keye shot (he / him), and Magua dropped to his death.

... next day the Delaware Indians had a burial ceremony for

... the beautiful maiden, and brave Uncas, the last of the

...cans.

35

Commas

A comma may or may not be used if an introductory phrase is short, so please note that there may be times when students feel a comma is needed and it is not shown (or vice versa).

Add commas where they belong in the sentences below.

Wow, that roller coaster was really fast!

After locking the house, I realized I had left my keys inside.

I have a nice red coat, but I wore my sister's warm, fuzzy jacket.

Yes, those energetic, spunky ponies are fun to watch.

We are going to the mall and then to the grocery store.

36

Edit this passage from *The Strange Case of Dr. Jekyll and Mr. Hyde* by adding commas where they belong.

There are 8 errors in this passage.

Mr. Utterson and Mr. Richard Enfield went for a walk together every Sunday. The two lived in London and were relatives. On one of these very walks, the pair found themselves at a cellar door. It reminded Mr. Enfield of an incident that he had witnessed on that same street. He shared the story with Mr. Utterson.

He had been walking down this street when he had seen a most disturbing thing. A little girl had been running to get the doctor, and she had collided with a disfigured man. Instead of helping the girl up, the man had trampled right over her and continued on his way. Outraged, Mr. Enfield had dragged the man back to the scene, where the girl's family and the doctor had gathered. Rather than calling the police, the angry group had demanded that the selfish man pay the girl's family. The man had agreed. He had gone into the cellar door and had come back with a check signed by another man, one who was very respectable. Mr. Enfield didn't say who that man was, but he did share the name of the rude, selfish man.

His name was Mr. Edward Hyde.

37

Semi-Colons

Add commas and semi-colons where they belong in the sentences below.

You can fold the towels, and I will fold the sheets.

This is my room; that one belongs to my sister.

My uncle likes spaghetti; I prefer lasagna.

Isabelle was tired but did not go to sleep.

The fireman drove away, but the policeman stayed at the scene

Our dog is missing; there is a reward for whoever finds him.

I need to go to the post office to mail a letter; stop at the store to buy lettuce, milk, and cheese; and run to the bank to cash a che

38

Edit this passage from *The Strange Case of Dr. Jekyll and Mr. Hyde* by adding commas and semi-colons where they belong.

There are 9 errors in this passage.

Mr. Utterson, a lawyer, was very troubled by the story. Although he had never met Mr. Hyde, he had heard the name before. One of his friends, Dr. Henry Jekyll, had given Mr. Utterson his will. In the will Jekyll stated that in the event of his death or disappearance, all of his possessions were to be given to Mr. Hyde. Mr. Utterson hadn't liked the will before; he liked it even less after hearing Mr. Enfield's story about Mr. Hyde.

Mr. Utterson was determined to meet Mr. Hyde. He walked by the cellar door many times, waiting in the street to catch a glimpse of the mysterious man. One dreary evening he saw a man unlocking the cellar door. The small man had an evil, disfigured appearance. Mr. Utterson disliked him at sight. When Mr. Utterson politely introduced himself, Mr. Hyde was very unfriendly. He asked Mr. Utterson how he knew him. Mr. Utterson replied that he had found out from Dr. Jekyll.

The man spat out, "I'm certain he has told you nothing about me!" Mr. Hyde whirled around angrily; then he entered the cellar door.

39

Review Time!

Edit this passage from *The Strange Case of Dr. Jekyll and Mr. Hyde*

There are 13 errors in this passage.

After Mr. Hyde disappeared inside the mysterious door, Mr. Utterson decided to visit Dr. Jekyll. His house was right around corner from the cellar door Mr. Hyde had entered. Mr. Utterson knocked on Dr. Jekyll's door. Poole, the butler, answered the d and said the doctor was not at home.

As he was leaving, Mr. Utterson realized that the cellar door w actually an entrance to Dr. Jekyll's house. The house was arra in such a way that there appeared to be two separate buildings they were actually connected. Mr. Utterson couldn't understand how Dr. Jekyll could be friends with the evil Mr. Hyde. He came the conclusion that Edward Hyde was blackmailing Dr. Jekyll fo some unknown reason.

Two weeks later Mr. Utterson had the chance to talk to Dr. Jek He decided to be honest; he told the doctor he was worried abc his friendship with Mr. Hyde. Dr. Jekyll told the lawyer not to be worried. He said he could be rid of Mr. Hyde at any time.

40

100

Quotes

se note that when students are editing, missing quotation marks count
ly one error although students will always add them in pairs.

capital letters and punctuation to the sentences below.
ather said to sweep the driveway and rake the yard.
ppy birthday!" <u>A</u>unt <u>S</u>adie shouted. "<u>H</u>ow old are you now?"
nk," <u>M</u>r. <u>S</u>chutt said, "it's going to rain."
at's for supper?" I asked. "<u>L</u>eftovers," my mom replied.

41

Edit this passage from *The Strange Case of Dr. Jekyll and Mr. Hyde*.

There are 12 errors in this passage.

Almost a year later a terrible crime was committed in <u>L</u>ondon. Sir Danvers Carew, a highly-respected man, was murdered. A maid happened to see the whole thing from her window. The murderer was a man she had seen before. She was certain that it was M<u>r.</u> Hyde!

Mr. Utterson took the police to Mr. Hyde<u>'</u>s house. The house was completely ransacked. There were clothes strewn about and evidence of burned papers. The police also found part of a cane, which was the murder weapon. Mr. Hyde (was / were) gone.

Mr. Utterson went to Dr. Jekyll's house that same day. He was worried that Mr. Hyde might be after Dr. Jekyll too.

"<u>I</u> have no idea where Mr. Hyde is," Dr. Jekyll said. "<u>W</u>e (is / are) no longer friends."

Dr. Jekyll also said that he had received a letter from Mr. Hyde. He showed the letter to Mr. Utterson. It said that <u>M</u>r. <u>H</u>yde was grateful for Dr. Jekyll's kindness and that (he / him) had left London.

42

---

his passage from *The Strange Case of Dr. Jekyll and Mr. Hyde*.

are 11 errors in this passage.

e passed, and still Mr. Hyde was not captured. With the
nce of the evil man, Dr. Jekyll became a new person. He
me very sociable, involved himself in charitable work, and
d friends over often. Mr. Utterson was glad to see that Mr.
's influence over Dr. Jekyll had disappeared along with the
himself.

e day Mr. Utterson went to visit <u>D</u>r. Jekyll. Poole answered the
and said that the doctor didn't want any visitors. Although Mr.
son returned many times, the butler always informed him that
ekyll didn<u>'</u>t want to see anyone. He had shut himself up in his
.

Utterson decided to visit Dr. Lanyon, another friend of his and
ekyll's. When Mr. Utterson arrived, he was surprised to see
Dr. Lanyon looked terribly ill! <u>T</u>he doctor explained that he had
red a terrible shock and didn't think he would recover. He
ed to talk about Dr. Jekyll at all.

e week later Dr. Lanyon died. He [left] a letter for Mr.
son, but the lawyer was not to open it until the death or
ppearance of Dr. Jekyll.

43

Edit this passage from *The Strange Case of Dr. Jekyll and Mr. Hyde*.

There are 14 errors in this passage.

Mr. Utterson and <u>M</u>r. <u>E</u>nfield were out for another one of their <u>S</u>unday walks. They passed by Dr. Jekyll's house. Mr. Utterson saw his friend sitting by one of the windows. He called out a greeting, which Dr. Jekyll returned. Then Dr. Jekyll's smile changed into a look of horrible suffering, and he quickly turned away from the window. The two men were very disturbed<u>;</u> they agreed not to speak about what they had seen.

Some time later Poole came to see Mr. Utterson. He was worried about his master.

"<u>I</u>'m afraid that something bad has happened to Dr. Jekyll," Poole began.

"<u>L</u>ike what?" Mr. Utterson asked.

"<u>P</u>lease, Mr. Utterson, come back to the house with me. I want to show you something," Poole replied.

Mr. Utterson agreed to go back to Dr. Jekyll<u>'</u>s house with the butler.

44

Midterm

Edit this passage from *The Strange Case of Dr. Jekyll and Mr. Hyde*.

There are 15 errors in this passage.

Poole explained that Dr. Jekyll had shut himself up eight days ago and hadn't come out since. He knocked on the door and told Dr. Jekyll that Mr. Utterson had come to see him. The weak, angry voice that called back (was / were) not Dr. Jekyll's. This was what Poole had wanted Mr. Utterson to see for himself. Poole [thought] that someone had killed Dr. Jekyll and was still in the room! He had worked for Dr. Jekyll for twenty years; he knew that the voice did not belong to his master.

Mr. Utterson and Poole decided to break into the room. It was the only way to know if Dr. Jekyll was still alive. They began to break through the door with an axe. They heard a scream of terror. Then there was quiet. When they made it through the door, they saw the body of Edward Hyde. He had killed himself before they could question (he / him). They looked all over for Dr. Jekyll, but he was nowhere to be found. He had disappeared!

Mr. Utterson [found] a letter with his own name on it on the table.

Adjectives

Circle all of the adjectives in the sentences below.

Josie dug a big hole in the soft dirt, but Ryan's hole was bigger.

Many people enjoy the unique sound of Irish music.

That flock of wild geese is louder than a busy street.

On vacation this year, we spent several days at a California bea

---

Read this passage from *The Strange Case of Dr. Jekyll and Mr. Hyde*. Circle as many adjectives as you can find.

Mr. Utterson left Dr. Jekyll's messy house and returned to his own. Now that Dr. Jekyll had disappeared, Mr. Utterson could read the mysterious letter Dr. Lanyon had left behind.

The letter explained the disturbing event that had shocked the doctor. One evening Dr. Lanyon had received an urgent letter from Dr. Henry Jekyll. It said that he was in trouble and needed Dr. Lanyon's help. Dr. Jekyll wanted Dr. Lanyon to go to his London house and bring back a little drawer, which contained a certain fluid and some powder. Someone would then come to Dr. Lanyon's house to get them. Dr. Lanyon had done as Henry Jekyll had asked. That same night a small, evil-looking man had come to the door and asked for those items. When Dr. Lanyon had given him the liquid and powder, the ugly man had mixed them together and drank them. Then, right before Dr. Lanyon's eyes, the man had transformed into Dr. Jekyll!

Edit this passage from *The Strange Case of Dr. Jekyll and Mr. Hyde*

There are 11 errors in this passage.

After reading Dr. Lanyon's letter, Mr. Utterson opened the lette from Henry Jekyll. It explained everything that had happened.

Dr. Jekyll had been very interested in the two different person-alities he recognized in (himself / themselves). The first was h "good" person, the doctor who was respected by his friends and charitable deeds. The second was his "evil" personality, whose secret thoughts and desires Dr. Jekyll had simply tried to hide a ignore. He had [begun] trying to separate the two personalities By drinking a certain chemical concoction, he had one night ac transformed into his "evil" self, which he named Edward Hyde. Whereas most people are a mixture of good and evil, Edward H (was / were) pure evil. Because this personality had been ign for so long, Edward Hyde was much smaller and weaker than D Jekyll.

Dr. Jekyll [drank] the concoction whenever he felt like releasin his evil side. Disguised as Edward Hyde, he was free to do whatever he wanted. Then he could drink the liquid to turn bac into Dr. Jekyll, and Mr. Hyde would simply disappear.

Page 49

this passage from *The Strange Case of Dr. Jekyll and Mr. Hyde*.

e are 10 errors in this passage.

Jekyll's evil nature had gradually gained strength. Then one
Dr. Jekyll had turned into Mr. Hyde just by thinking an evil
ght! He was so startled by this transformation that he vowed
r to release his evil side again. However, the desire built up
e of him until one day he again became Edward Hyde. The
had become so great that Mr. Hyde had killed Sir Danvers
w that same night. Dr. Jekyll had no choice but to banish
ard Hyde forever, for he was now a criminal and could no
er show his face freely.

two months Dr. Jekyll was back to his normal self. Then
ard Hyde [broke] through again. He had become too strong to
nored. Dr. Jekyll was forced to keep himself shut up in his
e. He no longer had control. Whenever he went to sleep or
a weak moment, he became Mr. Hyde. During one of his last
ds as Dr. Jekyll, he had written a new will leaving everything to
tterson. When Poole and Mr. Utterson had come to check on
him), he had killed himself. It was the only way to get rid of
vil Mr. Hyde.

49

Page 50

Edit this passage from *A Tale of Two Cities*.

There are 14 errors in this passage.

It was the year 1775. Crime was rampant in England, and the
common people of France were suffering from extreme poverty.
The rulers and nobles of France, however, lived in great comfort
and riches. They were unsympathetic to the peasants in their
country, and they lived lavishly with no regard for their poor
countrymen.

A man from London, Mr. Lorry, was traveling to Paris. He was a
loyal employee of Tellson's Bank, which had branches in both Paris
and London. A young woman, Miss Lucie Manette, joined him in
Dover. She had been told that Mr. Lorry had information regarding
her father, who had died before her birth.

Indeed, Mr. Lorry had some difficult news. Her father was not
dead; he had been in prison for eighteen years on false charges.
He had recently been released and was in the care of one of his
former servants. Mr. Lorry offered to accompany Lucie and Miss
Pross, Lucie's guardian, on their journey to find Dr. Manette and
bring him home to London.

50

Page 51

Adverbs

e words can function as adverbs or prepositions. If it is an adverb, it
ot be followed by a noun or a pronoun. For example, in the sentence "I
hind," "behind" is an adverb. In the sentence "I fell **behind** my
s," "behind" is a preposition because it is followed by a noun, "sisters."
bs often come right before prepositions, as in the sentence, "I fell
d with my brother." Students should understand this before trying to
e adverbs on the next page (52). They will get more practice and
on on the prepositions page (56).

important that students understand that "not" is an adverb because it is
common and is often buried in a contraction.

lete the sentences below by writing adverbs in the blanks.
ers will vary.

___quickly, daily___ .   She talks ___slowly, often___ .

s __really, not__ dirty.   He snores __loudly, repeatedly__ .

walks clumsily. I walk __more/less clumsily__ than she does.

ays badly, but I play even ___worse___ .

51

Page 52

Read this passage from *A Tale of Two Cities*. Circle as many adverbs as you can find.

Mr. Lorry was an old acquaintance of Lucie's father. He was the
one who had graciously taken little Lucie to England when her
mother had died many years before.

Lucie and her companions finally arrived at the Defarge's wine
shop, where Lucie's father was living. Mr. Defarge had been a
servant of Dr. Manette's in the past. He was now letting the doctor
stay in one of his rooms. Mr. Lorry and Lucie followed Mr. Defarge
inside. When they entered Dr. Manette's room, they saw an old
man sitting upright at a workbench. The man was diligently making
shoes. He did not recognize Mr. Lorry, and he referred to himself
simply as "One Hundred and Five, North Tower." He was very
startled by Lucie's presence, and he spoke of how she reminded
him of his wife.

Lucie spoke to her father tenderly and promised to take care of
him.

52

Edit this passage from *A Tale of Two Cities*.

There are 14 errors in this passage.

Five years later Lucie and her father (was / were) living a pleasant life in London. Dr. Manette had come back to his senses under his daughter's faithful, tender care. The Manettes were in a courtroom, where Charles Darnay, a Frenchman, was being tried for treason. Executions were common in England in those days, and Darnay was expected to be found guilty. He was charged with conspiring to help the French king in wars against England.

Several [witnesses] were called to testify. The first, John Barsad, repeated the accusations against Darnay and said that he had seen him with a list of names of English soldiers. Incidentally, Lucie had also seen and spoken with Charles Darnay five years ago on a ship bound from Paris to England. She testified that she had seen him talking with other Frenchmen and passing papers back and forth, but she didn't know what the papers said or what the conversations were about. She said that she hoped her words would not harm the prisoner, for he had been very kind to her and her father.

53

Edit this passage from *A Tale of Two Cities*.

There are 12 errors in this passage.

Another witness was called to the stand. He claimed that he h seen Darnay traveling and gathering information. The witness insisted that the man he had seen was definitely the prisoner. Darnay's lawyer, Mr. Stryver, pointed to another man and asked to remove his wig. When the man did so, the crowd was stunne He looked just like Charles Darnay! This coincidence weakene last witness's testimony enough to get the prisoner released. Lu Dr. Manette, Mr. Stryver, and Mr. Lorry gathered around Charles Darnay and congratulated him.

That evening Mr. Stryver was sitting in his office with Mr. Sydn Carton, the man who looked like Charles Darnay. Mr. Stryver w successful lawyer; Mr. Carton served simply as the lawyer's cle Mr. Stryver believed Sydney could be successful if he applied himself, but Sydney argued that he was too prone to drinking an would never be a good man. He blamed it simply on natural ra Mr. Lorry, Mr. Stryver, Mr. Carton, and Mr. Darnay became goo friends of the Manettes and visited them regularly.

54

Edit this passage from *A Tale of Two Cities*.

There are 10 errors in this passage.

In France a man known as Monsieur the Marquis was traveling home to his chateau. He had been at a party with other rich, well-to-do citizens. Like the others, Monsieur the Marquis did not work, but he lived richly and oppressed the peasants. He cared nothing for their welfare and felt no guilt about his lifestyle. The peasants, meanwhile, were becoming angrier every day over their intense oppression.

Charles Darnay was the nephew of Monsieur the Marquis. He visited his uncle, and they argued. Charles hated the way the nobles lived, but his uncle only cared about his own comforts. Charles told his uncle that he was going to live in England and work for his money. He did not want to live in France and bear the shame of his family's wickedness. That was why he had changed his name and left France.

That night Monsieur the Marquis (was / were) murdered by a peasant!

55

Prepositions

In order for students to tell whether a prepositional phrase functions as adjective or an adverb, they should find the word it modifies. If it modifi noun or pronoun, the prepositional phrase functions as an adjective. If modifies a verb, adjective, or adverb, it functions as an adverb.

Underline the prepositional phrases. Identify them as adjectival o adverbial.

I got a letter from my grandma.	adjectival
My friend looked around.	no prep. phra
She walked with purpose.	adverbial
The path winds through the garden.	adverbial
Kitchens with oak cabinets are nice.	adjectival

56

l this passage from *A Tale of Two Cities.* **Underline the ositional phrases and circle the objects of the prepositions.**

ɔther year passed. Charles Darnay became a French tutor in and. He fell in love with Lucie, and he shared his feelings with ather. Dr. Manette approved of the match.

arles was not the only one who loved the beautiful girl. Sydney on also loved her, and he told her so one night. He said he v she could never love someone of his character, but he wanted ll her that she had affected him in a way he had never thought ible. He told Lucie that he loved her enough to give his life to someone she loved beside her. Sydney asked her not to tell ne about their conversation, and he said he would never tion it again.

me time later Charles and Lucie were married. On the morning eir wedding day, Charles told Dr. Manette his real name and he was. Dr. Manette promised to keep his secret.

arles and Lucie continued to live with Dr. Manette. They had a tiful daughter, and they named her Lucie. They lived many y years together in England.

57

Edit this passage from *A Tale of Two Cities.* Identify the underlined prepositional phrases as adjectival (adj.) or adverbial (adv.).

There are 8 errors in this passage.

Meanwhile, the country of France was in turmoil. Mr. and Mrs. Defarge, who lived just outside of Paris (adv. - modifies outside), were among the many disgruntled peasants. Their wine shop had been a meeting place for the oppressed poor (adj. - modifies place) to gather and share information for many years. While Mr. Defarge was committed to their cause, Mrs. Defarge was far more determined. By 1789 the peasants had reached their boiling point. Led by the Defarges, (they / them) stormed the Bastille, a French prison. They killed the prison officers and released their fellow countrymen.

Within three years the peasants ruled France. The nobility had all either been killed or imprisoned or had fled from the country (adv. - modifies fled). Instead of restoring peace, the peasants continued in their rage (adv. - modifies continued). Their fight against oppression took an ugly turn. They (was / were) now imprisoning and executing innocent people without giving them fair trials. Large numbers of people were killed each day by the angry mob of peasants (adj. - modifies mob).

58

this passage from *A Tale of Two Cities.*

e are 11 errors in this passage.

h all of the turmoil in France, the Paris branch of Tellson's Bank a mess. In 1792 Mr. Lorry was called upon to travel to Paris usiness. On the night he left, Charles Darnay was visiting him. .orry had a letter for Marquis St. Everemonde of France, and les Darnay offered to deliver it. Only Charles and Dr. Manette v that Charles was actually the Marquis of St. Everemonde. e letter was from a man who was a servant to Charles Darnay. ad been put in prison by the peasants because he worked for ity. Charles [felt] that he had no choice but to go to Paris help his faithful servant. He knew that France had become a erous place, but he did not know just how bad it was. Charles e a letter to Lucie and a letter to Dr. Manette. He hoped to e them some pain by leaving before they knew what he was g. Then he left for Paris. He thought that the peasants would ect (he / him) because he had turned his back on his title and coming back of his own free will.

59

Edit this passage from *A Tale of Two Cities.*

There are 14 errors in this passage.

Charles was arrested as soon as he arrived in Paris. The peasants had passed new laws and given themselves the power to imprison others.

Dr. Manette, Lucie, her daughter, and Miss Pross traveled to Paris as soon as they learned about Charles's arrest. Dr. Manette was convinced that he could help Charles. Because he himself had been wronged by the nobles and imprisoned falsely for many years, he was accepted by the peasants as one of their own. However, he was unable to use his power to get Charles released. Charles was held in prison for over a year, but Lucie and her father still had hope that he would be freed. Many others were being executed every day. They were lucky that Charles was still alive.

Finally the peasants set a date for Charles's trial. On the day of the trial, it was revealed that Charles had been imprisoned based on the charges of three different people. The three who had denounced Charles were Mr. Defarge, Madame Defarge, and Dr. Manette!

60

Direct and Indirect Objects

Identify any direct objects (DO) or indirect objects (IO) in the sentences below.

The doctor examined Ethan's knee (DO).

My friend told me (IO) a secret (DO).

Juan bought his mother (IO) and father (IO) a present (DO).

She baked her family (IO) some cookies (DO).

61

Edit this passage from *A Tale of Two Cities*. Identify any direct or indirect objects in the underlined sentences.

There are 9 errors in this passage.

 Dr. Manette instantly denied the statement (DO). However, Mr Defarge had a letter that Dr. Manette had [written] while he was prison. In the letter Dr. Manette told the story of how he had be arrested. Many years ago, two brothers who (was / were) nob men had come to the doctor for help. They showed him (IO) a young woman (DO) and her brother (DO). Both were dying. Dr Manette learned that the brothers had taken the peasant girl fro her family. When her brother came to rescue her, they had wounded (he / him) with a sword. Dr. Manette (was / were) deeply troubled. Before he could report the matter, Dr. Manette been kidnapped by the brothers and thrown in jail. At the end o the letter, Dr. Manette denounced the brothers (DO) and their families (DO). Little did he know that one of the brothers had a who would grow up to be an honest man. That man was Charle Darnay, who was now married to Dr. Manette's own daughter!

 The peasant girl and boy mentioned in the letter were the brot and sister of Madame Defarge. That was why the Defarges had denounced Charles and had him arrested.

62

Edit this passage from *A Tale of Two Cities*.

There are 13 errors in this passage.

 The peasants were outraged by the crimes detailed in the letter. They decided that Charles Darnay would be executed the very next day for the suffering his family had caused the peasants. Dr. Manette could do no more for his son-in-law.

 Meanwhile, Sydney Carton arrived in Paris. He met with Mr. Lorry and gave him clear instructions to take the Manette family back to London the next day. Sydney had found John Barsad, the man who had testified against Charles Darnay at his first trial. He knew the spy had been lying, and he threatened to report him. John Barsad agreed to help Sydney get in to the prison to see Charles.

 The next day, just two hours before Charles was to be executed, Sydney went to visit him. He traded clothes with Charles, and then he caused him to faint. John Barsad took Charles, who was disguised as Sydney, to Mr. Lorry and the Manettes. Sydney was executed in Charles's place. He died in peace, knowing that it was a [better] thing than he had ever done before. He [knew] that Lucie would remember his words, "to keep someone she loved beside her."

63

Edit this passage from *The Merry Adventures of Robin Hood*.

There are 12 errors in this passage.

 By the time Robin Hood was just a young man, he could shoo arrow more skillfully than any other man. In Robin Hood's eighteenth year, the Sheriff of Nottingham announced that he w holding a shooting contest. Robin Hood set off from his own to of Locksley towards Nottingham to participate in the contest. O way Robin Hood came upon fifteen men. Seeing the youth with his bow and arrows, the men began to tease him. No young m likes to be teased about his manhood, and Robin Hood quickly challenged the loudest man to a shooting contest. Robin Hood [won] fair and square; the man refused to pay him. Instead, he shot an arrow at Robin Hood. Robin Hood sent one back. The man dropped down dead, and Robin Hood fled into Sherwood Forest. He felt sick and full of sorrow for his actions.

 Robin Hood was now an outlaw! He remained hidden in Sherwood Forest, for he could no longer live in town. The sher offered two hundred pounds for his capture.

64

this passage from *The Merry Adventures of Robin Hood.*

e are 14 errors in this passage.

he first year that Robin Hood lived in <u>S</u>herwood <u>F</u>orest<u>,</u> many
r [men] came to join him. These men were good<u>,</u> honest men
fled to the forest for one of two main reasons. Some of them
wanted for killing the king<u>'</u>s deer. The law stated that the
belonged to the king<u>,</u> and anyone caught shooting one was
sted. It didn't matter how poor or hungry or desperate they
. The second reason men came to join Robin Hood was that
had been made poor by the dishonest and oppressive rulers.
y of the barons<u>,</u> abbots<u>,</u> knights<u>,</u> and other officials imposed
taxes and unfair fines on the common people.
bin Hood's band of outlaws [grew] to around a hundred in
ber. The common people learned to love them<u>.</u> Robin Hood
his merry men took the wealth away from those who were
essing the poor and returned it to the needy. No one who
e to <u>R</u>obin <u>H</u>ood for help was turned away.

65

Circle the correct words in the sentences below.
This is a (good / well) movie. I like it better (than / then) that one.
Do you know (who's / whose) scarf this is? It is (real / really)
warm.
(Can / May) I see that stuffed toy? It looks like a (real / really)
animal.
He told the story (good / well). It had an inspiring (affect / effect)
on us.

66

---

this passage from *The Merry Adventures of Robin Hood.*

e are 10 errors in this passage.

e day Robin Hood came to a (real / really) narrow bridge.
as he began to cross, a tall stranger started crossing from the
side. The bridge was not wide enough for two men. After
ing about (who's / whose) duty it was to step aside<u>,</u> they
ded they would fight with their staffs until one of them knocked
ther into the water. They struggled for over an hour before the
an finally succeeded in knocking <u>R</u>obin <u>H</u>ood into the stream.
n Hood congratulated the stranger. The stranger had fought
d / well), and Robin Hood was very impressed by his skill.
an / Then) Robin Hood asked the man to join his band of merry
  The stranger<u>'</u>s name was <u>J</u>ohn <u>L</u>ittle. He was at least seven
tall<u>,</u> and he was wider (than / then) any man Robin Hood had
met. The merry men renamed the newcomer Little John. He
me Robin Hood's right-hand man and [closest] friend.
e John was not the only man Robin Hood recruited. Whenever
n Hood came upon a likable<u>,</u> skilled man, he asked (him /
) to join his band of merry men and share in their adventures.

67

Edit this passage from *The Merry Adventures of Robin Hood.*

There are 14 errors in this passage.

   The Sheriff of Nottingham had not forgotten about Robin Hood.
After a few different attempts to catch him, he [came] up with a
(real / really) clever plan. He decided to hold a shooting contest
and offer a prize that Robin Hood couldn<u>'</u>t resist. He knew Robin
Hood would want to prove his skill.
   On the day of the shooting match<u>,</u> the <u>S</u>heriff of <u>N</u>ottingham didn't
see Robin Hood anywhere. The contest continued until only the
three best archers were left. These three were Gilbert<u>,</u> Adam<u>,</u> and
an unknown beggar. The crowd cheered loudly for Gilbert and
Adam<u>,</u> but the beggar won. The sheriff congratulated the beggar
and gave him a golden arrow.
   "<u>I</u> declare<u>,</u>" he said, "<u>y</u>ou shoot [better] than Robin Hood, (who's /
whose) too much of a coward to even show his face!<u>"</u>
   That evening the Sheriff of Nottingham was feasting when an
arrow [flew] through the window. A scroll was attached. It read,
"Today you gave a golden arrow not to a beggar, but to none other
(then / than) Robin Hood."

68

107

Edit this passage from *The Merry Adventures of Robin Hood.*

There are 12 errors in this passage.

The Sheriff of Nottingham was very angry that Robin Hood had outsmarted him. He tried many times to capture the outlaw, but it seemed that Robin Hood was simply too clever. As for Robin Hood, he decided to teach the sheriff a lesson.

Nearly a year after the shooting match, Robin Hood set off towards Nottingham. He met a butcher and bought his clothes, meat, and cart. Robin Hood dressed up in the butcher's clothes and went to Nottingham to sell the meat. He [sold] it very cheaply to the poor and the widows.

After he'd sold all of the meat, Robin Hood saw the Sheriff of Nottingham. Robin Hood invited him to a feast. The sheriff didn't recognize Robin Hood and followed him willingly. Robin Hood took him to Sherwood Forest to his band of merry men. Then he took off his disguise. The sheriff was angry but could do nothing. After sharing a grand feast with his guest, Robin Hood took the sheriff's ill-gotten money and sent him on his way.

69

Edit this passage from *The Merry Adventures of Robin Hood.*

There are 13 errors in this passage.

Some time later Robin Hood [sent] out six of his men. (They / Them) needed a rich man to come and feast with them in order get more money. The men returned with a guest, but he was no wealthy. He was a minstrel, and he was deeply distraught. His name was Allan Dale. He was in love with a beautiful maiden w loved him in return. However, the girl's father had pledged her an old knight. They were to be married in just two days.

Robin Hood vowed to help. Taking a handful of men, he set o find a holy man. He came into the company of Friar Tuck, who agreed to help. On the morning of the wedding, they went to th church. When Robin Hood approached the old knight, he humb stepped aside. The maiden's father, however, was not as easy persuade. As Robin Hood had brought Friar Tuck to marry the couple, the father was left with no choice. Robin Hood paid hin (good / well) to give his blessing anyway.

Allan Dale and Friar Tuck both joined Robin's band of merry n

70

Modifiers

Rewrite the sentences below so that the meanings are clear. Answers will vary.

I put a flower in my hair, which smelled very good.
I put a flower, which smelled very good, in my hair.

Walking underneath the tree, my umbrella ripped.
Walking underneath the tree, I ripped my umbrella.

She noticed a girl standing by the fence with a ponytail.
She noticed a girl with a ponytail standing by the fence.

Dad handed me a present with a big smile.
With a big smile, Dad handed me a present.

His neck was stiff after counting all of the stars in the sky.
His neck was stiff after he counted all of the stars in the sky.

71

Edit this passage from *The Merry Adventures of Robin Hood.* Find underline one misplaced modifier and one dangling modifier.

There are 15 errors in this passage.

One fine autumn day Robin Hood and Little John set off in different directions. They were trying to find a guest to share th feast that was rich. Robin Hood met a knight, but he was not ri In fact, he was deeply in debt. His name was Sir Richard, and told Robin Hood his story. Sir Richard's son had been involved jousting accident; now Sir Richard was being forced to sell his and everything he had to keep his son out of prison.

Little John, on the other hand, brought the Bishop of Hereford who was very wealthy. After the merry men feasted with their tv guests, Robin Hood collected payment from the bishop. He too one third for the band, gave one third to Sir Richard, and return the other third to the bishop.

Sir Richard was very grateful to Robin Hood and his men. Vo to repay Robin Hood, the money was counted carefully. The ne year, true to his word, Sir Richard came back to Sherwood Fore and paid back every penny he had borrowed.

72

Edit this passage from *The Merry Adventures of Robin Hood*.

are 10 errors in this passage.

bin Hood and his merry men were enjoying the cool shade of
wood Forest when a visitor arrived. It was none other than the
en's page, and he came bearing an important invitation from
en Eleanor herself! King Henry was holding a shooting match,
the queen wanted Robin Hood and some of his men to come.
n Hood [chose] Little John, Will Scarlet, and Allan Dale to
mpany him.
g Henry didn't know that Queen Eleanor had invited Robin
d. On the day of the competition, she made a bet with the king.
bet that she could find three men who could beat the king's
] three archers. The king agreed to the wager.
en the best three archers were left from the king's men, the
n called out Robin Hood and his friends. The king was very
ised to see the outlaws, but (he / him) had given the queen
word.

73

Edit this passage from *The Merry Adventures of Robin Hood*.

There are 12 errors in this passage.

Six new targets were [brought] out for the competition between the
king's archers and the outlaws. Will Scarlet shot against Hubert of
Suffolk for third place. Although Will shot very well, Hubert won the
round. The king smiled at the queen; the queen smiled back.
Little John was competing against Tepus for second place. Two of
Tepus's arrows hit the center, but all three of Little John's found the
middle of the target.
Lastly, Robin Hood faced Gilbert to see who would win first place.
Gilbert shot first and hit the middle circle with all three of his
arrows. It was the best shooting the crowd had seen all day. The
king was confident that he would win the bet. However, Robin
Hood shot his three arrows so close to the center of the target that
they looked like a single arrow!
Taking first and second prize, Robin Hood and his men were
declared the winners of the competition. Queen Eleanor won the
bet!

74

this passage from *The Merry Adventures of Robin Hood*.

are 14 errors in this passage.

ny months had passed since the shooting match. King Henry
died, and King Richard now sat on the throne. Robin Hood
his band of merry men continued to hunt, feast, and seek
nture.
Sheriff of Nottingham had realized that he couldn't capture
n Hood himself, but he still wanted him [caught]. The sheriff
a notorious outlaw, Guy of Gisbourne, to find and kill Robin
d. The two met one day in the forest. They had never seen
other before, and Guy didn't know that he was speaking to
n Hood. Guy introduced himself and told Robin Hood why he
come. At this Robin Hood revealed his identity. They drew
swords. After a long, vicious fight, Robin Hood killed his
nent. Although Robin Hood took no satisfaction in his victory,
new Guy had been a terrible man responsible for many deaths.
bin Hood disguised himself as Guy of Gisbourne and rescued
John, who had been caught by the sheriff that same day.

75

Labeling Sentences

**In the sentences below, underline the subjects once and the verbs
twice. Circle the adjectives. Mark the adverbs (ADV), the direct
objects (DO), and the indirect objects (IO). Cross out any prepositional
phrases.**

            ADV   DO
Joshua spotted nearly a dozen tadpoles in the pond.

            IO   DO   DO
Mom passed me the warm French bread and soft butter.

                    ADV   DO
After supper Ruth carefully painted a picture of a brilliant sunset.

                        ADV   ADV ADV
The snowman by our sidewalk did not melt very quickly.

76

109

Edit this passage from *The Merry Adventures of Robin Hood*.

There are 14 errors in this passage.

Now King Richard had heard about Robin Hood and his merry men, and he very much wanted to meet them. He was impressed by the [stories] he had heard about their kindness. He and six of his men disguised (himself / themselves) as friars and journeyed to Sherwood Forest. They counted on Robin Hood and his men inviting them into the forest for a feast, and that was exactly what happened.

When the feast was over, Robin Hood demanded the usual hefty payment from their guests. The king lifted his hood. Robin Hood and his men [knelt] at once. King Richard spoke to the band. He asked them to come into his royal service. He invited Robin Hood, Little John, Will Scarlet, and Allan Dale to accompany him back to London. The rest of the men could stay in the forest as royal rangers. All of them (was / were) pardoned for their crimes!

Robin Hood and his men heartily agreed to the king's terms. The Sheriff of Nottingham was vexed indeed when the king returned home with Robin Hood at his side!

Edit this passage from *Twenty Thousand Leagues Under the Sea*.

There are 13 errors in this passage.

It was the year 1866 when ships first began to report strange sightings of a mysterious object in the seas. Although at first th reports were scoffed at and dismissed, it soon became clear tha did exist. Numerous ships recorded sightings and even collisio with the unknown form. The mysterious object was widely discussed. All rumors and gossip aside, there were two possib explanations. Either the object was an unknown sea monster o incredible size and speed, or it was a man-made submarine bui better (than / then) any other known vessel.

I, Pierre Aronnax, arrived in New York just as these events we unfolding. As the assistant professor at the Museum of Natural History in Paris, I had spent six months conducting a scientific expedition in Nebraska. Because of my reputation as an exper marine biologist, my opinion was widely requested. After review the facts, I published an article stating my position. I believed t the mysterious monster was a narwhal of enormous size and po

---

Edit this passage from *Twenty Thousand Leagues Under the Sea*.

There are 15 errors in this passage.

The majority of the general public agreed with my assessment. After one particular ship was badly damaged by the mysterious menace, it was clear that the creature must be found and killed. The American government took action at once. A man named Commander Farragut was chosen to lead the hunting expedition. A fast frigate, the *Abraham Lincoln*, was loaded with all kinds of guns, cannons, and harpoons.

As I was in New York at the time of the ship's departure, I was asked to join the expedition. I had been looking forward to returning home to France, but I could not turn down this unique opportunity. I left immediately for the ship with my faithful servant and companion, Conseil.

Commander Farragut and his crew were determined to kill the giant narwhal. Among the men on the ship was a Canadian named Ned Land. He was a skilled harpooner, and he was confident in his abilities. However, he was one of the only men on the ship who didn't believe that such an animal existed.

Edit this passage from *Twenty Thousand Leagues Under the Sea*.

There are 9 errors in this passage.

A reward of two thousand dollars was offered by Commander Farragut to the first man to spot the monster. Everyone on boa the *Abraham Lincoln* kept a careful watch on the seas, but thre months passed without a sighting. Just before we [gave] up, N Land spotted the creature.

It was a short distance from our ship, and it was glowing. It w least two hundred and fifty feet long and shot water over a hun feet into the air. We pursued the monster for nearly a day with success. It possessed remarkable speed and maneuverability. That night we got close enough for Ned to try and spear it. He hurled his harpoon at the creature, but it bounced off the hard surface with a loud clang.

The creature shot water over our ship. I tumbled into the cold black water below. When I made it back up to the surface, the *Abraham Lincoln* was too far away for me to signal. Just as I began to sink, a strong hand pulled me back to the surface. It Conseil, my trustworthy companion. He had seen me fall overb and had jumped in after (I / me).

Diagramming Sentences

am the sentences below.

e of the clouds were very dark.

young girl fell down the flight of stairs.

liant rainbow appeared in the sky above our heads.

e Georgia beaches are beautiful in the early spring.

ousin on my mother's side swam across the dirty river.

81

Edit this passage from *Twenty Thousand Leagues Under the Sea*.

There are 10 errors in this passage.

   Conseil was as calm as always. While one of us floated on his back, the other one swam and drove (we / us) forward. We took turns to conserve our strength until we could be rescued. We kept up this routine for nearly two hours. Just as my strength gave out, Conseil's cry of help was answered. He continued to push us forward. Much to our surprise, it was Ned Land who had called to us. He had also been swept overboard; he was now stranded on the back of the monster.

   Ned helped us onto the floating object, and I began to inspect the surface. I realized that I had been wrong about the monster. It wasn't a narwhal after all. It was a man-made vessel of steel, and we were sitting on top of it. The moment it [dove] back under the water, we would all be lost!

   Just then an iron panel opened. Eight men appeared. They dragged us into the vessel and left us in a dark chamber. (We / Us) had no choice but to sit and await our fate.

82

---

his passage from *Twenty Thousand Leagues Under the Sea*.

are 16 errors in this passage.

ort while later two men came to visit us. They turned on a nd spoke in an unintelligible language. I explained who we in French and English, but they made no response. Conseil German without any result. The men left the room, and a steward brought us supper. The food was exquisite. After our fill, we fell asleep. The next day one of the same men to visit us again.

fessor Aronnax, will you join me?" he asked. He spoke in ct French.

companions and I were shocked! The man continued to . He informed us that we were his prisoners, and he had ed to let us live. However, we would never be allowed to the submarine. His existence under the sea was unknown, e wanted to keep it that way. We had no choice but to accept ecision. He introduced himself as Captain Nemo and (than / again invited me to join him. The captain was well- ainted with both my name and my work.

83

Edit this passage from *Twenty Thousand Leagues Under the Sea*.

There are 14 errors in this passage.

   Captain Nemo gave me a complete tour of his craft, the *Nautilus*. The large submarine was actually a very luxurious vessel with a dining room, library, drawing room, and comfortable living quarters. The rooms were extremely well-furnished with tasteful furniture and expensive works of art. Captain Nemo was clearly a very rich man.

   The captain also explained to me how the *Nautilus* was capable of such speed and agility. It was powered by electricity. While I had only heard of small amounts of power being generated in this way, the captain had figured out a way to generate much larger amounts. He was obviously a very smart, well-educated man as well. Captain Nemo showed me a variety of instruments, some familiar and some unknown, which helped guide the *Nautilus*. It rose to the surface each day to renew its oxygen supply. A small boat affixed to the top of the craft enabled the captain to take short fishing or pleasure trips.

   In this fashion Captain Nemo and his crew traversed the globe, explored the ocean's depths, and collected fascinating specimens.

84

Edit this passage from *Twenty Thousand Leagues Under the Sea*.

There are 10 errors in this passage.

   Despite being prisoners, we enjoyed a comfortable life on the *Nautilus*. Our meals consisted of excellent fare provided by the ocean and cooked to perfection by Captain Nemo's chef. The library offered hundreds of volumes for us to read. A huge window in the drawing room gave (we / us) a captivating view of the ocean and the abundant life therein. When we surfaced we (was / were) allowed to stand on top of the vessel and breathe the fresh air. On occasion Captain Nemo invited us to explore the ocean's floor with him. We [wore] special suits complete with breathing devices. I was able to study the depths of the sea like never before.

   Captain Nemo was a strange man. We enjoyed a certain level of companionship and shared a mutual feeling of respect. Some days I spent many hours talking with and learning from Captain Nemo; other times I didn't see him for long periods of time. For unknown reasons, the captain had abandoned the world of [men] and preferred to live free from rules and laws under the ocean.

85

Combine each group of sentences below into one sentence. Answ will vary.

I play baseball. I am on a Little League team. I play third base
I play third base on a Little League baseball team.

Nathan is building a fort. The fort is in a tree. Marcus is helpin Nathan. They are almost finished.
Marcus and Nathan are almost finished building a tree fort.

Brenda made cookies. They are sugar cookies. There are four dozen.
Brenda made four dozen sugar cookies.

I have to wrap a present. It is for my sister. It is her Christmas present.
I have to wrap a Christmas present for my sister.

Our neighbors have three dogs. They also have two cats. The are five kids in the family. Our neighbors live in a big house. It gray.
Our neighbors live in a big gray house with their five kids, three dogs, and two cats.

We have two fruit trees. They are in our backyard. They are c trees.
We have two cherry trees in our backyard.

86

Edit this passage from *Twenty Thousand Leagues Under the Sea*.

There are 11 errors in this passage.

   We spent many months exploring oceans, gulfs, and seas all over the world. I was enthralled by the experience and began writing notes for a new book on marine life. This unique lifestyle afforded me the opportunity to indulge in my personal passion. Conseil was content, as always, just to be close by my side. He appreciated the wonderful sights nearly as much as I did. Ned Land, however, grew weary of life on the submarine. He was a hunter by trade and was tired of being confined under the water. His temper worsened each week, and he was determined to escape as soon as possible.

   Although I was enjoying our journey, I agreed that we should escape if we ever got the chance. It was clear that Captain Nemo was never going to free us, and I very much wanted to return with my notes to my homeland and family. Our only hope was that we would journey close enough to a civilized country. We would steal the small boat and paddle as far as we could. Hopefully a ship would spot us and come to our rescue.

87

Edit this passage from *Twenty Thousand Leagues Under the Sea*.

There are 14 errors in this passage.

   We had been on the *Nautilus* for over four months. During th time we had [seen] many new and wonderful sights. We (was were) currently heading for the South Pole. I was amazed at t captain's sense of adventure.

   The *Nautilus* moved along the surface of the water. When we reached the Great Ice Barrier, I thought that our adventure wou have to be forsaken. The captain, however, was determined to the first to reach the South Pole. He proposed that we go und the ice. We would fill the submarine's reservoirs with oxygen s that we could stay underwater longer.

   Over a day and a half later, we rose to the surface and took o bearings. We had reached the South Pole! Captain Nemo pla his flag.

   On our way back, a mountain of ice fell into the ocean, blockin our path. We were trapped! Working in shifts, we used picks t chip away at the ice. It took us days, and our oxygen reserve quickly depleted. By the time we broke through and rose to the surface, we had all nearly suffocated.

88

his passage from *Twenty Thousand Leagues Under the Sea.*

e are 12 errors in this passage.

uple of months later we had another deadly experience. Ned
, Conseil, and I (was / were) looking out the window when we
e] upon a group of giant cuttlefish. The ugly, squid-like
ures were well over twenty feet long and had eight enormous
covered with hundreds of suction cups. They were angered
r presence.

Nautilus stopped with a sudden shock. Captain Nemo
ed the drawing room with a somber look on his face. A cuttle-
ad [gotten] tangled up with the submarine. We had no choice
rise to the surface and fight the monstrous creature in order
ain control. Each man was armed with an axe; Ned Land
a harpoon. As soon as the panel was opened, the cuttlefish
two of its giant arms into the vessel. It grabbed the closest
an and dragged him out of the ship. Captain Nemo let out an
yell; he began to attack the disgusting creature with his
et. An intense battle followed. We defeated the cuttlefish, but
ere unable to save the unfortunate seaman.

89

Edit this passage from *Twenty Thousand Leagues Under the Sea.*

There are 15 errors in this passage.

Captain Nemo wept at the loss of his crew member. He retreated
to his room, and I didn't see him for many days. The *Nautilus*
wandered about with no set course.

After ten months on board the *Nautilus,* Ned was desperate to
escape. One day he told me that we were going to escape that
very night. He had gone on top of the vessel that morning when it
had surfaced; he had spotted land about twenty miles away.
Whether we made it or not, we agreed that it (was / were) worth
the risk.

We were in the process of detaching the small boat that night
when we heard a loud cry. The *Nautilus* was heading into a giant
whirlpool! No ship had ever escaped from this powerful force. Our
hearts seemed to stop in terror. My head [struck] something hard,
and I sank into darkness.

When I woke up, I was lying in the house of a fisherman. Ned
Land and Conseil were sitting beside me. Our survival was a
mystery. An even [greater] mystery was the fate of Captain Nemo
and his extraordinary *Nautilus.*

90

113